CW00435426

Spotlight on Writing

A teacher's toolkit of instant writing activities

Glynis Hannell

Routledge
Taylor & Francis Group

LONDON AND NEW YORK

First published 2009
by Routledge
2 Park Square, Milton Park, Abingdon, Oxon OX14 4RN

Routledge is an imprint of the Taylor & Francis Group, an informa business

© 2009 Glynis Hannell

Typeset in Sabon by
Florence Production Ltd, Stoodleigh, Devon
Printed and bound in Great Britain by
MPG Books Ltd, Bodmin

British Library Cataloguing in Publication Data
A catalogue record for this book is available from the British Library

ISBN10: 0–415–47308–X (pbk)
ISBN13: 978–0–415–47308–8 (pbk)

Contents

Other books from Routledge by Glynis Hannell

CHAPTER 1

Introduction

Writing: an essential skill

Written language plays an important part in learning, socialisation and employment. We write letters and emails to friends, organisations and businesses, we prepare reports, we keep records, we answer questions and we make enquiries using written language.

Anyone who can write well can communicate effectively across a broad range of situations. This opens up opportunities in education, training and employment that are not so readily available to those who lack confidence or skills in written communication.

Poor writing skills

In the classroom writing skills are of significant importance. Much pupil learning is encapsulated in written form. Pupils write assignments, complete projects, do homework and sit tests and examinations. In every one of these situations the pupils' abilities are judged on the basis of what they have written down. This can seriously disadvantage some pupils whose poor writing skills can disguise their true level of understanding or competence.

Poor writing skills can also be part of more global difficulties with language and literacy, and in this case the barriers to success are substantially increased. Considerable frustration and loss of confidence can result and a pupil may feel that their deficits are, quite literally, in 'black and white' for all to see.

Your inclusive classroom

An effective classroom writing programme will take into consideration the needs of pupils who may need individualised materials, explicit teaching and opportunities for extended practice to build their skills. An inclusive approach to the teaching of writing delivers a double advantage to pupils. First, a flexible, inclusive approach will mean that all pupils will receive appropriate teaching and make the best progress possible. Second, the advantages of good writing skills will filter into every aspect of the pupils' lives in school and beyond.

If classroom instruction fails to be sufficiently inclusive or appropriate to the pupils' needs, the pupils' writing skills will fail to develop and the cycle of disadvantage and negatives increases. However, when success is experienced, confidence, interest, motivation and enjoyment often follow.

Writing is a complex skill and it follows that many pupils in your classroom will need a high level of effective, inclusive teaching, over an extended period of time, in order to be able to reach a reasonable level of competence.

What is 'writing'?

The difference between spoken and written language

Many pupils think that writing is simply an exact replica of spoken language. However, as adults we know that skilled written language can be quite different from spoken language. In comparison to spoken language, written language usually has:

- a wider, more expressive vocabulary;

- a more careful selection of words;

- more formal vocabulary, with less use of slang, colloquialisms and so on;

- more abstract language;

- more formal sentence structures;

- better organisation of ideas;

- properly constructed sentences;

- a monologue style in which the writer is the only 'speaker';

- a 'voice', where the reader is assigned the role of listener (often with little prior knowledge of the topic assumed);

- regular use of compound sentences;

- stricter adherence to the rules of grammar;

- opportunities for editing, correction and polishing before completion;

- total reliance on the written word (no body language or facial expressions to supplement the message);

- a less spontaneous, more considered use of language;

- a need for correct spelling and punctuation.

The ability to think objectively about written language is part of the process that is called *meta-linguistic awareness*. *Thinking* about writing is an important part of the writing process. In an inclusive classroom this skill is explicitly taught and practised.

Once pupils are able to think objectively about their own written language, they are on the way to becoming writers who can use words deliberately and skilfully. In turn, this capacity allows them to use written words as a powerful communication tool, not only producing quality written language themselves, but being able to read and evaluate written language that has been produced by other writers.

This book provides you, the teacher, with many activities, all expressly designed to help all your pupils develop an awareness of how to produce good written language.

Language difficulties and writing

Although this book is all about developing your pupils' skills in written language, it is important to remember that oral language is a crucial foundation for written work.

Pupils who have delay or difficulty in general language skills will almost inevitably run into similar difficulties with written language. Their difficulties with oral language may include:

- limited vocabulary;

- difficulties in formulating sentences;

- problems in 'finding' words;

- poor organisation of what they want to say.

These limitations in oral language will usually lead to a mirror image of similar difficulties in written language. A pupil who has a limited oral vocabulary is likely to use a narrow range of words in their written language. A pupil who talks in a rambling, poorly organised way will very often produce written language that lacks organisation and structure.

Conversely, pupils with strong oral language skills, who already have a wide vocabulary and use language confidently and accurately, will be well equipped to perform well in written language.

As you will know, the book that you are reading at the moment is called *Spotlight on Writing: A teacher's toolkit of instant writing activities*. If you are interested in promoting your pupils' *oral* language skills as well as their written language skills, you will find it useful to obtain a copy of a companion book entitled *Spotlight on Language: A teacher's toolkit of instant language activities*, which is aimed at providing foundation work in oral language. The two books can be used in tandem to provide your pupils with a language enrichment programme that stretches across both oral and written language.

Spotlight on Writing: foundations of success

Using the right words

Words are, of course, the essential working materials of written language. Just as a craftsman such as an artist, engineer, carpenter or chef selects his materials and uses his tools skilfully towards a goal, so a skilled writer makes a careful and considered choice of words to obtain a particular result.

An unskilled writer may:

- write whatever words come into his or her head;

- assume that written words are a direct transcript of spoken language;

- rely on a very limited vocabulary of familiar words.

A skilled writer can:

- use words to give very exact information;

- use a range of parts of speech, such as verbs, adverbs and adjectives, as working tools;

- plan ahead to use particular words when writing;

- think about what they are writing and how they are using words;

- deliberately choose a particular word from a range of alternatives;

- consciously reject some words as poor choices;

- manipulate words to create specific effects.

Chapter 2 gives teachers a range of activities designed to promote pupils' awareness of the way in which words can be used as working tools in writing. This helps to develop every pupil's writing skills.

Sentence building

An unskilled writer will often:

- use words according to a prescribed formula, for example using worksheets as the basis for writing *I see the boy*, *I see the girl*, *I see the dog*, *I see the pig*;

- write one long string of words or phrases, without any structure or punctuation;

- use a long string of very short sentences;

- use incorrect grammar, for example *Ken and Barry is going to work* or *Yesterday I go to the park*.

A skilled writer will be able to:

- avoid unnecessary repetition;

- use a range of sentence structures according to need;

- integrate several pieces of information into one complex sentence;

- create sentences that are grammatically correct.

Chapter 3 is designed to give your pupils plenty of practice in structuring sentences correctly. Specific activities are provided to promote the use of conjunctions, to develop skills in putting words in the right order and to build well-constructed sentences.

Writing facts and information

There are many forms, or genres, of written language, and each requires pupils to have a particular skill set. Writing facts and information demands that pupils can write clearly and succinctly, taking the needs of their readers into consideration.

Unskilled writers tend to:

- give a list of facts without an attempt to order them in a logical sequence;

- assume the reader has the same knowledge base as the writer, for example using 'he' without letting the reader know who 'he' is;

- give every single piece of information on the topic regardless of whether it fits the question or not;

- write vague statements that do not really highlight the key facts;

- fail to clarify what is fact and what is opinion.

Skilled writers are usually able to:

- organise their information into a logical structure;

- write so that the reader can relate to what is being said;

- write for a specific purpose, editing out irrelevant material;

- clarify what is essential information and give that precedence;

- make a clear distinction between fact and opinion.

Chapter 4 provides pupils with activities that require clear, factual writing and also, in one instance, an opportunity to make the distinction between fact and opinion. This chapter also helps to develop very controlled, precise writing.

Creative writing

Creative writing is a genre that challenges some pupils. While they may enjoy listening to or reading fiction, actually producing their own creative ideas and using interesting or new language may be very daunting.
Unskilled writers often:

- use a limited vocabulary of basic words;

- find difficulty in thinking of new or imaginative ideas;

- stay with 'safe' concrete ideas;

- have difficulty creating a plot that has a beginning, a middle and an end;

- repeat familiar plots over and over again.

Skilled writers can often:

- create an imaginary situation by the skilled use of words;

- think up unusual or interesting ideas;

- take risks and explore new directions each time they write;

- develop a plot that moves logically to an interesting conclusion.

Chapter 5 is focused on creative writing, giving pupils some interesting 'start-up' ideas, and promoting the use of more adventurous language. Some pupils may find it really hard to come up with imaginative ideas and may find it much easier to think in literal, practical ways. In this chapter, inclusive activities are aimed at stimulating discussion, brainstorming and sharing ideas, so that the less imaginative or creative pupils can be inspired by the more creative ones. The end result is that all pupils can feel comfortable at making an attempt at creative, imaginative writing.

Writing fluency

Some pupils have interesting ideas and good language skills and yet they fail to produce written work that meets expectations. They may write very slowly and with a lot of effort and yet produce messy and disappointing work. Writing is a skill that demands very good integration between brain and hand. Words that are formulated mentally have to be transformed into physical movements so that they can be written down. For some pupils this is a difficult and slow process.

There may be some pupils who are anxious about putting their thoughts down on paper, perhaps fearing that their ideas may seem 'silly' or 'wrong' when written down. Others are overly worried about correct spelling or neat handwriting. All these pupils may sacrifice writing fluency for the security of knowing that what they write is correct.

For both groups, slow, disjointed writing can become something of a habit, where the pupil is simply not accustomed to writing more fluently. Although the use of a computer can sometimes alleviate physical writing difficulties, this is not always the answer. Some pupils find it difficult to learn to type quickly enough and others are still worried about making themselves look foolish when they put their own ideas down in print.

Other pupils may experience difficulty in formulating the ideas that they want to write down, so for them slow writing is part of a bigger picture, where difficulties producing ideas or words are the cause of the writing block.

The best writing is often produced by a quick approximation while the ideas are flowing, followed by a more careful revision of the draft once the main ideas have been written down.

Chapter 6 has activities designed to foster fluent writing, perhaps by breaking down one pupil's habit of slow, cautious writing or by helping another pupil practise writing skills.

Editing

Checking for errors and revising what has been written are essential steps in completing any written work.

Unskilled writers often:

- believe that writing is complete as soon as it is physically finished;

- believe that a quick check of spelling is the most that is required.

Skilled writers:

- always check their work;

- check for grammatical errors as well as spelling mistakes;

- reorganise the sequence of what they have written if needed;

- rewrite all or part of their work if needed;

- look at the 'big picture' and check how well their work meets the set requirements;

- try to find ways to improve what they have written;

- cut out irrelevant information or comments.

Chapter 7 contains a series of passages for your pupils to edit and rewrite. Although there are certainly errors in punctuation and spelling, these passages also provide you and your pupils with the opportunity to discuss and work on sentence structure, grammar, expression, word use, order of information, relevance and so on.

It is always easier to spot mistakes in other people's work than your own! Your pupils will learn a lot from working to correct these passages. Working through the poorly written passages and rewriting will help to develop skills that pupils can apply to their own work in the future.

Effective, inclusive teaching

Let us briefly look at some of the key elements of effective, inclusive teaching:

- Teacher and pupils, talk, explore, discuss and work on writing together.

- There are many opportunities for pupils to learn from each other.

- The teacher provides individual assistance when pupils need this.

- Every pupil can participate in the same type of activity.

- Classroom activities are individualised to meet pupils' differing skill levels.

- Extra support and scaffolding are given when pupils need them.

- Stereotypes do not limit individual pupils' opportunities.

- All pupils have the chance to take on new challenges and extend themselves.

- Pupils are taught how to think about writing.

- Pupils are taught writing and learning strategies.

- Sub-skills of writing are taught to all pupils.

- Teaching is explicit and focused.

- Understanding is developed through examples, discussion and explanation.

- All pupils have sufficient practice to master what they have been taught.

- Mistakes or incorrect answers are viewed as valuable teaching opportunities.

- Writing activities engage the pupils' interest.

- Activities offer disadvantaged pupils enrichment as well as skills.

Spotlight on Writing in your inclusive classroom

Differentiated learning materials for inclusion

Each of the activities is presented at three levels of difficulty. Level 1 is the easiest level, Level 2 intermediate and Level 3 the most difficult. There is deliberate overlap between the three levels to allow for easy transitions between one level and the next.

One activity can be used to suit a wide range of pupils within a mixed ability class. For example, a teacher may use Level 2 for most of the class, but direct the more able pupils to continue on with Level 3 items, while their younger or less able classmates work on Level 1 items. All pupils will be doing exactly the same activity, but at different levels of difficulty.

The gradual increase in difficulty levels and the overlap between levels helps teachers to provide *inclusive activities* in their classrooms.

Pupils with language or learning difficulties

Pupils who experience difficulty with writing may benefit from introductory work on an easier level than some other pupils. This is often sufficient to prepare them to cope with the more *challenging* items that follow. The teacher can make a decision on whether to:

- provide additional teaching support to help the pupil complete the activity; or

- if the first level is successfully completed, have the pupil progress to the more difficult levels of the same activity; or

- if the first level has only been completed with assistance, have the pupil move to a similar activity, but at the same level of difficulty as before, and provide assistance as required on the new activity.

For example, Carol and Charles have both been given Level 1 of *Better verbs* (Activity 2). Carol coped with this quite easily, so the teacher decides that she can now move on to Levels 2 and 3 of this same activity.

Charles, however, clearly found Level 1 quite challenging, so he is not yet ready for the more difficult Level 2. Instead, the teacher uses Level 1 of *Just one word* (Activity 1) as a teaching tool and spends time talking to Charles about each item in turn. In doing so, the teacher provides extra *scaffolding* and *support* for Charles.

The teacher might also use this *explicit teaching* technique the next time Charles has a similar activity drawn from another publication. The teacher might also create a similar worksheet based on the curriculum that the class is following. This provides Charles with fresh learning materials and further opportunity to work in this area of written language.

A key principle for inclusive teaching is that teachers vary the amount and style of support given to pupils of varying abilities. For example, while one pupil may be able to answer a question without any prompts or hints, another may need the teacher to give more scaffolding and assistance, such as:

- discussion

- leading questions

- helpful comments, hints or clues

- multiple choice options.

For example, if Josie cannot find a better word than *went* for the sentence *The horse went into the forest*, the teacher can ask 'Do you think "The horse trotted into the forest" or "The horse walked into the forest" is best?' The resultant learning is still valid, but has required more structure to achieve the end result.

Pupils with advanced development

The more advanced pupils often gain considerable insight into a task by participating in the easier items, in which the *thinking* processes and the *strategies* used are usually more concrete and overt. For example, in *You can edit!* (Activity 20) the strategy of checking for repetition may be more obvious at the easier levels but readily reapplied at the more difficult levels.

Pupils who have advanced writing development usually thrive on activities that challenge them. Teachers can readily select a range of activities and/or levels to provide the bright pupil with *individualised activities* that will extend their writing skills. For example, a very advanced six-year-old might start with Level 2 of the selected activity and even move through to Level 3 if able to do so.

Interactive, inclusive and explicit teaching

Unlike many other pupil workbooks, *Spotlight on Writing* activities are intended to be used as *explicit* teaching materials, and as the basis of *interaction* between teacher and pupil(s). Teachers may often find that the younger and less able pupils benefit from participating in classroom *discussion* and attempts at the more difficult levels, classroom interaction and discussion will give them good models for successful completion of the activities. This provides an opportunity for the pupils to be *challenged* and perhaps to break a *stereotype* of what they can and cannot do.

Although all the activities in this book have all been presented as *written language* activities, classroom discussion is seen as an essential part of the *inclusive learning* process. By talking about the tasks, working with the teacher and bouncing ideas off one another, pupils are well prepared for the written language aspect of the task once they begin to work individually. For example, brainstorming ideas for *Keep writing* (Activity 13) will help to foster an exchange of ideas and increase the opportunities for all pupils, with a range of individual differences, to be *included* in the same learning activity. Such discussions promote the development of thinking, language, writing and related learning in all students.

Many activities can be used as the basis for the *explicit teaching* of a range of language-related skills. For example, *Repairing sentences (1)* and *(2)* (Activities 7 and 8) are very valuable exercises in sentence building. They provide the teacher with a good opportunity to teach language skills through discussion and trial and error attempts at sentence repair.

For example, the class may all be discussing how to repair the written sentence *I was . . . up in the middle of the night by a loud noise*. Larry might suggest that the sentence could be repaired as *I was woked up in the middle of the night by a loud noise*, giving the teacher an opportunity to talk about the verb *wake* and, with the pupils, to work out that *woken* is a good fit for the sentence.

Many of the activities help to build the *sub-skills* of writing and this assists the teacher in identifying *individual pupils'* areas of difficulty and strength. For example, Louis may have poor physical writing skills and be easily *stereotyped* as having widespread difficulties with written language, but then prove to be very skilled at editing, showing that his insight into the writing process is in fact advanced in some ways.

The process of deliberately choosing one word and rejecting another is a good example of a sub-skill that is *explicitly taught* in 'Using the right words' (Chapter 2) and 'Editing' (Chapter 7).

These activities help to extend the writing skills of pupils who, for whatever reason, have limited skills in using interesting vocabulary in their own writing.

In some situations, a pupil may be able to cope with an activity orally but be unable to complete this same activity in writing. If this is the case, the activity can be treated as an oral language activity in its own right. Alternatively, the teacher can assist with the recording of the pupil's oral responses. In either case, the pupil will have had a useful learning experience in the use of language but will have had the mode in which the task was completed *individualised* to suit his or her particular difficulties.

Writing – a key skill for life

Learning about written language is a lifelong process that not only provides valuable academic benefits but also can become a source of endless fascination and delight. Understanding how written language can be manipulated helps pupils to express themselves in writing. It also helps them to appreciate the skills and craft of other writers whose work they will encounter throughout their lives.

A classroom in which writing activities are based on lively discussion, interesting learning and plenty of fun will ensure that your pupils truly enjoy learning about writing.

Users' guide to *Spotlight on Writing*

Ethical and inclusive teaching

All the reading activities in this book have been carefully written to provide teachers with ethical, responsible and inclusive teaching materials. Although the main purpose of each item is to promote the development of your pupils' writing skills, the materials also promote social responsibility, personal resourcefulness and thoughtfulness towards others.

The use of language related to popular culture (such as superheroes or fantasy), the supernatural, specific religious beliefs or inappropriate role models has been avoided where possible. However, in *Mystery and adventure* (Activity 15) there are some occasional references to *magic, giants, time machines* and so on, simply because of the nature of the writing genre being introduced. Teachers can use their discretion with regard to these items.

Flexibility

Teachers can draw activities from any chapter, in any order according to the needs of a particular group of pupils. For example, a teacher may want to concentrate on 'Writing fluency' and so may use several activities from Chapter 6 in quick succession. Another teacher may be aware that some of her pupils have limited skills in word use and so may decide to draw on the activities in 'Using the right words' (Chapter 2).

Ease and speed of use

The book is ready for instant teaching. The only preparation required is for the teacher to preselect the appropriate activity for the class, group or individual.

The activities provide a variety of valuable writing experiences that can form the basis of a single lesson or series of lessons.

These activities are often quick to do and are ideally suited to short sessions, in which one or more levels of items can be given to the class as a whole, or a selected group of pupils as required. Many activities are also perfect for a quick, intensive burst of writing when there are only a few minutes to spare.

Teaching notes

The teaching notes at the start of each activity provide teachers with a brief rationale for the activity and practical teaching hints. In some situations suggested correct answers, sample answers or guides are provided for the teacher's convenience.

Suitability for parents or teaching assistants

Teachers may find that parents will welcome the activities in this book for fun-based learning at home. The teaching notes help any adult to use the activity to maximum effect and enable paraprofessionals or even volunteers (such as parents assisting in a learning support programme) to use the activities designated by the pupil's teacher.

Suitability for classroom, small group or individual lessons

The activities in this book all lend themselves to classroom, small group or individual lessons, in which pupils and teacher work on the items collaboratively. The varied nature of the activities allows teachers to select those that can form the basis of an individualised programme for a particular pupil or group of pupils with special needs.

All the activities are intended to provide pupils with explicit teaching of the key sub-skills of writing. As such, they are suitable for pupils with special needs as well as mainstream pupils. The teacher can adjust the degree of individual guidance and support according to the needs of the pupils he or she is working with.

Supplementing a remedial programme

While the book is not intended as a specialist written language programme, teachers and others working with pupils can use the activities as supplementary work to be done at home and at school.

Emphasis on language

Writing is a high-order form of language and we cannot separate out writing from other forms of language. You will find that, while many activities throughout this book do require the pupils to write, many can be adapted or used as oral language activities. This is particularly useful when working with pupils with limited writing skills. Being able to complete a task as an oral language activity is a great foundation for the writing skills that will come later. It also means that the pupil can be fully included in the classroom activity, but working with the activity in oral rather than written form.

For example, if eight-year-old Tom is still at a very early stage of writing, he may well still be able to complete and really benefit from *Better verbs* (Activity 2) as an oral language activity. This activity will stand him in good stead as his writing skills advance.

Emphasis on print not illustrations

Illustrations are not used to support pupils' reading or writing in this book. Why is that? The reason is simple. In this book we are helping pupils to use printed words. We want to encourage the pupils to focus on the print and to do this we keep illustrations in the background, so that the pupils depend on the print itself.

Worksheets

Teachers are given permission to copy any activity for use with the pupils that they teach.

Most of the activities are composed of nine different tasks at each level. Sometimes it would be unreasonable to ask pupils to do more than one of the nine tasks suggested, for example there are nine *Mystery and adventure* (Activity 15) topics at each level, and clearly pupils will only be able to write one of the stories in any given lesson time.

In other situations, the teacher may be able to ask the pupils to complete all nine of the tasks at a particular level. For example, it may be quite realistic to ask pupils to create nine *Similes* (Activity 16) in a single lesson time.

Teachers can identify different levels of difficulty, or different volumes of work. For instance, one pupil may be asked to attempt only Level 1, or the teacher might circle the specific items in an activity that the pupil is required to complete. Alternatively, the teacher may set a given number of items to be completed, for example '*Choose any six questions from this sheet.*'

Teachers of pupils with special needs may find it useful to work through the activity with the pupil on one worksheet and then use a clean copy of the worksheet for the pupil to work through the same task again independently.

Making connections

All learning works best if it is connected with other learning. The exchange and cross-fertilisation of emerging skills that occur within a classroom can create a powerful network of interlinked learning.

The activities in this book are specifically directed at writing, but teachers will find that they can create links across the curriculum. For example, the class may have worked on several 'Editing' (Chapter 7) activities and these skills can be applied to written work from any area of the curriculum. Or a group of pupils may have worked on *Fact or opinion?* (Activity 12) and could use this experience to help sift out what is fact and what is opinion in science reports that they have written:

> Jenny said that she thought that the plant in the water was the best, but that was just her opinion. Margie said that the plant in the water was the tallest and had the most leaves and that was fact.

Follow-on activities

The activities are carefully constructed to provide pupils with appropriate writing activities. Many teachers will find it useful to devise other, similar activities concerning current classroom topics, using the activities in this book as a model. For example, 'Editing' (Chapter 7) provides practice in editing written passages. A teacher could easily make up similar passages to reinforce the skills being taught. The pupils could also, of course, simply use their own written work as an editing exercise.

Approximate age levels

There are no hard and fast rules about which level of activities should be given to children of a particular age. The activities are flexible and open to teachers to use in a variety of ways with a wide range of ages and abilities.

However, the following chart (see p. 16) gives a guide to the approximate levels usually appropriate for different age ranges and ability levels. This will vary somewhat according to the type of activity. For example, the creative writing activities can be very open-ended and so suit a wide range of age groups and ability levels. Conversely, some of the activities depend on more specific levels of skill and will be suitable for a narrower range of pupils who have skills at or around the level required for the particular tasks.

Indication of levels appropriate for given age ranges and ability levels

Age and ability ranges	Level 1	Level 2	Level 3
6 to 7 years			
average for age group	usually		
advanced	usually	usually	possibly
very advanced	usually	usually	usually
7 to 9 years			
significant difficulty	usually		
mild difficulty	usually	usually	
average for age group	usually	usually	possibly
advanced		usually	usually
very advanced		possibly	usually
9 to 12 years			
significant difficulty	usually	usually	
mild difficulty	usually	usually	possibly
average for age group		usually	usually
advanced		possibly	usually
very advanced			usually
12 years and above			
significant difficulty	usually	usually	possibly
mild difficulty		possibly	usually
average for age group		possibly	usually

Key:

usually suitable for age and ability	(dark shading)
possibly suitable for age and ability	(light shading)

CHAPTER 2

Using the right words

Thinking about language

One of fundamental 'stepping stones' towards good writing is the ability to select and use exactly the right word to make your work precise, interesting and varied. This chapter helps all your pupils to develop skills in using the right words.

Explicit teaching, involving class discussion, brainstorming and teacher guidance, will show pupils how to review, manipulate and improve their own written language by choosing better, more appropriate or more expressive words.

All the activities in this chapter focus on teaching pupils to stop and think about word use.

In some activities pupils are asked to think of appropriate words to fill in gaps, or act as substitutes for words already provided. For example, in *Better verbs* (Activity 2) the pupils have to replace the verb that is given with another verb that is more interesting. Through these activities pupils are introduced to the concept of being able to discriminate between words of similar meaning to refine their own written language.

In other activities the pupils are asked to use specified words or phrases. This is more difficult, because pupils have to create entirely new sentences containing the target word or phrase. For example, in *Adjectives and nouns* (Activity 4) the pupils are given phrases such as *huge leap* or *empty house* and are asked to insert these phrases into new sentences. This challenges sentence formulation skills and stimulates the pupils to write more complex and interesting sentences.

This chapter gives pupils practice in the use of:

- nouns
- verbs
- adjectives
- adjective + noun phrases.

Your pupils will certainly be using nouns and verbs already in their daily writing. The activities in this chapter help you to teach the pupils to use more interesting, appropriate or expressive nouns and verbs.

If you look at some of your pupils' spontaneous writing you may notice that they seldom use interesting verbs or adjectives. Other pupils, however, may already be quite adept at using a range of varied words. The activities in this chapter are specifically designed to promote every pupil's confidence and skill in the use of expressive words.

You will often find that, as with all the activities in this book, the most advantageous way to use the activities is to discuss, brainstorm and teach before you ask your pupils to write.

Activity 1: Just one word

Teaching notes

Pupils often write as they think, not stopping to consider that they could use better words to make their writing more succinct. *Just one word* alerts pupils to the possibilities of writing more clearly by using fewer words. The exercise includes both nouns and verbs.

There can be several possible answers. Here are some suggestions.

Level 1

1   kitten

2   forgot

3   stood

4   station

5   baker

6   palace

7   neighbour

8   family

9   pay

Level 2

1   rushed, dashed

2   grandparents

3   trod, stamped, stepped

4   winner

5   blinked

6   lost

7   soared

8   frightened, terrified

9   escalator

Level 3

1   cutlery

2   submerged

3   imitates

4   reptile

5   mare, filly

6   detective

7   dislike, hate

8   exhausted

9   rude

Activity 1

Just one word

LEVEL 1

Find one word to use in place of the phrase that is underlined. Write the new sentence out.

1 Lenny was given a <u>baby cat</u> for his birthday.

2 Jane <u>could not remember</u> how to do the puzzle.

3 Dad <u>put his feet</u> on the chair so he could reach the top shelf.

4 The dog went to the <u>place where the train stopped</u> to meet his master.

5 The <u>man who bakes the bread</u> has to get up very early in the morning.

6 The bluebird flew to the <u>building where the king lived</u>.

7 The <u>person who lives next door</u> will look after the dog for us.

8 My <u>mother, father, brothers and sisters</u> went to the circus.

9 Larry had to <u>give some money</u> for the ride on the pony.

Activity 1

Just one word

LEVEL 2

Find one word to use in place of the phrase that is underlined. Write the new sentence out.

1 Bob <u>ran quickly</u> to telephone for help.

2 Jenny visited her <u>grandmother and grandfather</u>.

3 The boy <u>put his foot</u> on the snail.

4 The <u>child who came first</u> was given a silver cup.

5 The owl <u>shut her eyes very quickly</u> when the sun came out.

6 They were <u>not sure where they were</u>.

7 The eagle <u>flew very high</u> in the sky.

8 The chicken was <u>feeling very scared</u> because the fox was near.

9 Their father met them by the <u>moving staircase</u>.

From: *Spotlight on Writing*, Routledge © Glynis Hannell 2009

Activity 1

LEVEL 3

Just one word

Find one word to use in place of the phrase that is underlined. Write the new sentence out.

1   They put out all the <u>knives, spoons and forks</u> on the table.

2   The hippopotamus can stay <u>under the water</u> for a long time.

3   Our parrot often <u>speaks in just the same way as</u> the teacher.

4   A crocodile is a <u>type of animal that lays eggs and is cold-blooded</u>.

5   The <u>girl horse</u> was called Molly.

6   The <u>person who solves difficult crimes</u> said 'This is a mystery.'

7   'I <u>really do not like</u> drinking sour milk,' said the little princess.

8   The animals were <u>so tired that they could go no further</u>.

9   The monkeys were <u>not well mannered</u> when they came to tea.

Activity 2: Better verbs

Teaching notes

Pupils, especially those with limited skills, may use verbs such as *went*, *said*, *got* and so on over and over again in their writing. Even though in everyday conversation it is quite usual to rely on this basic vocabulary of frequently occurring words, *Better verbs* teaches pupils that, in written language, more formal, varied and interesting verbs can be used to improve their written expression.

Discussion, brainstorming and teacher guidance are important parts of this activity.

There can be several possible answers. Here are some suggestions.

Level 1

1 ran, raced, rushed, strolled, rode

2 munching, chewing, nibbling

3 pour, rush, trickle, drip, leak

4 borrowed, chose

5 loves, enjoys

6 baked, created

7 dashed, rushed, chased, tore

8 chopped, sliced

9 climbed, leapt

Level 2

1 peeped, peered, glanced

2 trotted, galloped

3 shouted, screamed, yelled

4 sipping, slurping, gulping

5 pedalling, wobbling, rushing

6 repair, mend

7 screamed, squealed, shrieked, shouted

8 stretched

9 leaped, sprang, vaulted, hopped

Level 3

1 chew, munch, nibble

2 sighed, sobbed, whispered

3 grinning, beaming

4 rinse, scrub

5 toss, lob, hurl

6 swaying, rocking

7 tugging, hauling, yanking

8 howling, sobbing, snivelling

9 crouched, shrank, huddled

Activity 2

Better verbs

LEVEL 1

Look at the underlined word. Think of a more interesting word. Write the new sentence out.

1   I <u>went</u> to the park.

2   The sheep was <u>eating</u> the grass.

3   The water will <u>come</u> out of the hole in the bucket.

4   Becky <u>got</u> a book from the library.

5   Dad <u>likes</u> gardening.

6   Mum <u>made</u> a big chocolate cake.

7   Sam <u>ran</u> to the shop.

8   The girl <u>cut</u> the fruit into little pieces.

9   The cat <u>got</u> on to the wall.

Activity 2

Better verbs

LEVEL 2

Look at the underlined word. Think of a more interesting word. Write the new sentence out.

1 The children <u>looked</u> into the dark room.

2 The horse <u>went</u> into the forest.

3 Mum <u>said</u> 'Stop! That is very dangerous.'

4 Jon was <u>drinking</u> the hot milk.

5 The clown was <u>going</u> around on a bicycle.

6 Can you help me to <u>fix</u> this broken plate.

7 'Help, help!' she <u>said</u>. 'I am slipping off the roof.'

8 The gorilla <u>put</u> his arms out to reach the banana.

9 The boy <u>jumped</u> over the gate.

Activity 2

Better verbs

LEVEL 3

Look at the underlined word. Think of a more interesting word. Write the new sentence out.

1   The goat started to <u>eat</u> the lady's straw hat.

2   'I am so unhappy,' he <u>said</u>.

3   You could tell Kate was pleased because she was <u>smiling</u>.

4   You will have to <u>wash</u> that shirt to get the stain out.

5   <u>Throw</u> the ball as far as you can.

6   The trees were <u>moving</u> in the strong wind.

7   Grandfather was <u>pulling</u> the dog along on a lead.

8   The child could not stop <u>crying</u>.

9   They <u>bent</u> down behind the hedge so that the wolf would not see them.

Activity 3: Better adjectives

Teaching notes

Some pupils rely on a very limited range of adjectives (or describing words) in their writing. This limits their ability to create interesting written language. In *Better adjectives* the pupils are asked to substitute a new and better word for the one that has been used. Discussing the options can help all pupils to understand how written language can be manipulated and improved.

There are many possible answers. Here are some suggestions.

Level 1

1 huge, enormous, immense, gigantic, vast, massive, giant
2 delicious, tasty, scrumptious, yummy, delectable
3 interesting, fascinating, remarkable, exciting
4 fantastic, fabulous, great, wonderful
5 beautiful, lovely, gorgeous, attractive
6 delicious, tasty, scrumptious, yummy, delectable
7 beautiful, lovely, gorgeous, attractive
8 fragrant, spicy, delicious
9 soft, silky, warm, smooth

Level 2

1 disgusting, foul, revolting, horrible, nauseating
2 sizzling, boiling, scorching, blistering
3 lovely, beautiful, exquisite, charming
4 ancient, dilapidated, antique
5 delighted, overjoyed, thrilled
6 hideous, unsightly, repulsive, disgusting
7 miserable, wretched, glum, fed up
8 filthy, grubby, soiled
9 furious, annoyed, outraged

Level 3

1 unkind, horrid, cruel, wicked
2 wealthy, prosperous, affluent
3 favourite, beloved, treasured, precious, cherished
4 tiny, minute, miniscule, diminutive
5 impoverished, destitute, underprivileged
6 challenging, testing, tough, demanding
7 powerful, sturdy, strapping, muscular
8 ill, unwell, ailing
9 gentle, caring, thoughtful

Activity 3

Better adjectives

LEVEL 1

The adjectives are underlined. Find a better adjective and write the sentence out again with your new word.

1 Tom was scared of the <u>big</u> dog.

2 'This is very <u>nice</u> fruit,' thought the chimpanzee.

3 My teacher said 'I like this book because it is <u>good</u>.'

4 'Jump into the water, it feels <u>nice</u>,' said Dad.

5 Paul drew a really <u>cute</u> picture.

6 'I love this chocolate cake; it is <u>good</u>,' said Betsy.

7 The flowers in grandmother's garden were <u>pretty</u>.

8 There was a very <u>nice</u> smell in the kitchen.

9 The cat's fur felt very <u>good</u>.

From: *Spotlight on Writing*, Routledge © Glynis Hannell 2009

Activity 3

Better adjectives

LEVEL 2

The adjectives are underlined. Find a better adjective and write the sentence out again with your new word.

1   The food had mould on it and tasted <u>bad</u>.

2   The steam from the volcano was <u>hot</u>.

3   They walked beside a <u>pretty</u> lake.

4   The clown was riding a very <u>old</u> bicycle.

5   The giraffe was <u>happy</u> that her baby was not lost.

6   The <u>ugly</u> gorilla gave the lady a big hug.

7   The hen was very <u>unhappy</u> because it was raining.

8   They looked at the <u>dirty</u> clothes that the man was wearing.

9   The tiger was <u>cross</u> when he found he had lost his stripes.

From: *Spotlight on Writing*, Routledge © Glynis Hannell 2009

Activity 3

Better adjectives

LEVEL 3

The adjectives are underlined. Find a better adjective and write the sentence out again with your new word.

1 The king was very <u>mean</u> to the poor people in his country.

2 The man was so <u>rich</u> that he could buy anything he wanted.

3 The small doll was her <u>best</u> toy.

4 There was a <u>little</u> person coming from the cave.

5 The children in the refugee camp were <u>poor</u>.

6 The mountain climb was <u>difficult</u> in the snowstorm.

7 The horse was so <u>strong</u> that it could pull the heaviest cart.

8 So many people were <u>sick</u> that the show was cancelled.

9 Sam was always <u>kind</u> to the other kids in his class.

Activity 4: Adjectives and nouns

Teaching notes

Younger and less able pupils often use few, if any, adjective–noun phrases as they write. For example, a pupil might write *Sally put on her dress. It was blue* and not *Sally put on her blue dress. Adjectives and nouns* requires pupils to place an adjective–noun phrase into a sentence. This requires good language and writing skill and gives your pupils valuable writing practice.

There are many possible sentences. Here are some suggestions.

Level 1

1 Sally put on her blue dress.

2 The heavy box fell off the table.

3 They put on clean clothes before they went to school.

4 Tyler wished that he had a fast car.

5 The cat jumped over the high wall.

6 You have to buy new shoes when your old shoes wear out.

7 You can have an exciting ride on a train.

8 Sally had a delicious cake for her birthday.

9 The bear jumped into the cold water.

Level 2

1 The frog made a huge leap from the pond.

2 All the kids had very dirty hands.

3 The elephant put her enormous feet into the bowl of ice cream.

4 There was a lovely smell in the kitchen.

5 Tim heard a terrifying noise.

6 The car could not climb up the steep road.

7 The monkey hid in the narrow space behind the table.

8 They could hardly read the faded writing.

9 Pam was all alone on the deserted island.

Level 3

1 The children did not eat the scarlet berries.

2 In the bottom of the bag was an ugly toad.

3 The captain of the ship called out in a furious voice.

4 They did not dare to go into the empty house.

5 There were handprints on the damp wall.

6 They found a wrecked ship in the bay.

7 They put up a curtain to hide the gruesome scene.

8 The monkeys all screamed when they saw the poisonous snake.

9 The rescuers found the exhausted climber in a snow cave.

Activity 4

Adjectives and nouns

LEVEL 1

Look at these phrases and put each one into a sentence.

1 blue dress

2 heavy box

3 clean clothes

4 fast car

5 high wall

6 new shoes

7 exciting ride

8 delicious cake

9 cold water

Activity 4

Adjectives and nouns

LEVEL 2

Look at these phrases and put each one into a sentence.

1 huge leap

2 dirty hands

3 enormous feet

4 lovely smell

5 terrifying noise

6 steep road

7 narrow space

8 faded writing

9 deserted island

From: *Spotlight on Writing*, Routledge © Glynis Hannell 2009

Activity 4

Adjectives and nouns

LEVEL 3

Look at these phrases and put each one into a sentence.

1 scarlet berries

2 ugly toad

3 furious voice

4 empty house

5 damp wall

6 wrecked ship

7 gruesome scene

8 poisonous snake

9 exhausted climber

CHAPTER 3

Sentence building

From informal to formal language

In spoken language we can often use casual structures and informal expression to communicate our ideas. A pupil might say something like '*And there was this dog, this really big dog and and he jumped all over me and then my sister, she was scared and she screamed and and Mum came running out real fast.*' Such strings of short, simple phrases or 'run on sentences' can get a message across quite effectively when they are spoken.

However, in written language sentences need to be formulated using correct grammar and appropriate sentence structure. A written account of the dog attack (verbally described above) might read something like this when it is written down: *There was a very large dog jumping all over me. Then my sister screamed because she was scared. When Mum heard my sister screaming she ran out of the house as fast as she could.*

Pupils need to acquire several important skills in order to change their own informal, conversational language into correctly formulated written language.

The skilled use of joining words enables pupils to write succinctly and with greater precision. Joining words such *because, then* and *when* can transform a string of phrases and short, repetitive sentences into well-written language. *Joining words* (Activity 5) gives all your pupils practice in this important skill.

Many pupils rely on a simple format of sentence structure that they use over and over again in their own writing, such as *I went to the park, I went to school, I went home.* Learning how to write sentences with new and varied structures can be a real challenge for some pupils.

Words in order (Activity 6) helps your pupils to build skills in writing using a variety of sentence structures. The pupils have to rearrange the words to create a sentence that makes sense. This process will help your pupils to feel more comfortable using sentence structures that may not previously have been part of their own natural way of writing.

Your pupils will get extra practice in formulating sentences in the *Repairing sentences (1)* and *(2)* activities (Activities 7 and 8). In these exercises the pupils have to find one or more words that will 'repair' the sentence. The pupils will often have to sift mentally through various, alternative sentence structures until they find words that are a perfect fit. In doing this they will develop the ability to discriminate between sentences that are correctly structured and those that are not. This will help them to manipulate their own written language to create sentences that are easy to read, clear and well structured.

Activity 5: Joining words

Teaching notes

Young pupils often use short, simple sentences. In order to be able to write longer, more complex and more interesting sentences, the pupils will need to be able to use conjunctions (joining words).

Joining words gives pupils the opportunity to work with longer sentences, filling in the missing conjunction. This helps them to gain skill and confidence in handling longer, more complex sentences when they write.

Here are some suggested answers.

Level 1

1   and

2   if

3   or

4   for

5   until

6   because

7   so

8   when

9   after

Level 2

1   once, after, when

2   but

3   before

4   than

5   where

6   how

7   but

8   if

9   since

Level 3

1   nor

2   though

3   either

4   whether

5   while

6   both

7   either

8   although

9   also

Activity 5

Joining words

LEVEL 1

Put a joining word into the sentence so that it makes sense.

1 John played with the cat _____ the dog.

2 You can come to my house _____ you want to see my kitten.

3 Do you like apples _____ do you like pears best?

4 You can come _____ a ride on my scooter.

5 Here is your drink. Wait _____ it is cool before you drink it.

6 Be careful with the knife _____ it is very sharp.

7 Jenny had lost her pencil _____ she could not write her name down.

8 It gets dark _____ the sun goes down.

9 The dog ran _____ the cat.

From: *Spotlight on Writing*, Routledge © Glynis Hannell 2009

Activity 5

Joining words

LEVEL 2

Put a joining word into the sentence so that it makes sense.

1 You can come in _____ the floor has dried.

2 I don't have a hat _____ I do have an umbrella.

3 Wash your hands _____ you eat your breakfast.

4 This tree is much bigger _____ the other one.

5 I don't know _____ I put my library book.

6 Tell me _____ you managed to frighten the robber away.

7 Tom was very tired _____ he still ran all the way home.

8 You will win a prize _____ you get the best score.

9 The lion had not eaten _____ she had been back with her cubs.

Activity 5

Joining words

LEVEL 3

Put a joining word into the sentence so that it makes sense.

1   Neither Tahlia _____ Tom heard the sound of the glass breaking.

2   Joe was the strongest boy even _____ he was not very tall.

3   Bring _____ a plate of cakes or a box of biscuits.

4   I am not sure _____ to go to the zoo or the circus.

5   Sit down here _____ I finish off this sewing.

6   The monkey and the zebra were _____ afraid of the leopard.

7   You can have _____ strawberry ice cream or banana yoghurt.

8   I will let you watch TV _____ you know you are supposed to be in bed.

9   Fred not only broke his glasses, he _____ cut his knee.

Activity 6: Words in order

Teaching notes

Organising a set of words into a sentence is not always as easy as it seems! In *Words in order* your pupils will sometimes have to experiment with various sequences of words to find a sentence that makes sense and follows the rules of grammar. This helps to 'stretch' the pupils' capacity to formulate sentences. In turn these new-found skills in sentence building will help to develop your pupils' own writing skills.

Some items can have several correct solutions. Here are some suggestions.

Level 1

1   The hen laid ten eggs in the nest.

2   Trees give us shade in the summertime.

3   The little brown horse trotted down the road.

4   Kenny wished that he could fly.

5   Apples, bananas and oranges are all fruit.

6   The big bad wolf lived in the forest.

7   If you are sick you have to stay at home.

8   You can hear with your ears and see with your eyes.

9   Crocodiles have very strong teeth.

Level 2

1   The tiger has stripes and the leopard has spots.

2   Wool comes from sheep and makes warm clothes.

3   You can eat carrots cooked or raw.

4   Carpenters can make things out of wood.

5   Little lambs can be frightened in a storm.

6   It hardly ever rains in the desert.

7   Your hair and your fingernails grow all the time.

8   Beth wanted to have a pony ride for her birthday.

9   A group of elephants is called a herd.

Level 3

1   You need special equipment to climb Mount Everest.

2   You can see the moon clearly on a cloudless night.

3   Some boats have engines and some boats have sails.

4   The earth is round and circles the sun.

5   Polar bears live on the ice in the Arctic.

6   Maps are useful for showing you the correct route.

7   When the telephone rings it means someone is calling you.

8   Mark thought that he should offer to help the teacher.

9   Nurses and doctors work in hospitals to make sick people better.

Activity 6

Words in order

LEVEL 1

The words in these sentences are jumbled up. Sort them out and write the words in the correct order.

1   The ten laid hen eggs in the nest.

2   Give trees us shade in the summertime.

3   The horse down trotted the little brown road.

4   Kenny wished that he fly could.

5   Fruit are all apples, bananas and oranges.

6   The big lived in bad wolf the forest.

7   If you at home are sick you have to stay.

8   You can hear with your eyes and see with your ears.

9   Very crocodiles strong teeth have.

Activity 6

Words in order

LEVEL 2

The words in these sentences are jumbled up. Sort them out and write the words in the correct order.

1   The tiger and the leopard has stripes has spots.

2   Wool makes warm clothes comes from sheep and.

3   Carrots can you cooked or raw eat.

4   Carpenters can out of things wood make.

5   Little frightened in a can storm be lambs.

6   It ever rains in desert the hardly.

7   Your grow hair your fingernails all the time and.

8   Beth to have wanted a birthday pony ride for her.

9   A herd group of is a elephants called.

Activity 6

Words in order

LEVEL 3

The words in these sentences are jumbled up. Sort them out and write the words in the correct order.

1 You climb equipment to need special Mount Everest.

2 You clearly can see on a night the moon cloudless.

3 Some some engines and boats boats have have sails.

4 The circles earth the sun is and round.

5 Polar live bears on in the Arctic ice the.

6 Maps for are useful showing you correct the route.

7 When telephone you it means the someone rings is calling.

8 Mark that thought he offer to should the teacher help.

9 Nurses better and people hospitals doctors to make work in sick.

From: *Spotlight on Writing*, Routledge © Glynis Hannell 2009

Activity 7: Repairing sentences (1)

Teaching notes

Being able to repair a sentence with a missing word is an important skill. It helps pupils to develop an awareness of sentence structures that they probably would not yet use in their own writing. *Repairing sentences (1)* gives practice in verbs and verb tense. Copying the complete sentence out helps to build the pupils' familiarity with these new structures.

There may be several appropriate answers. Here are some suggestions. It is good to discuss the alternatives with your pupils to extend their word use and their awareness of how good word choice can improve their writing.

Level 1

1 is

2 went

3 are

4 was

5 going, hoping

6 fell, jumped

7 had, loved

8 ran

9 found, discovered

Level 2

1 will, may

2 drank

3 woken

4 swam

5 make, bake

6 feed

7 hid, put, placed

8 sent

9 stolen, taken

Level 3

1 catch, get

2 rode

3 risen

4 drove, travelled

5 grown

6 spoken

7 kept

8 brought, provided

9 left, departed

Activity 7

Repairing sentences (1)

LEVEL 1

There is a word missing in each sentence. Write the sentence out again and fill in the missing word.

1 My cat is indoors but my dog ——— in the yard.

2 Yesterday I ——— to the zoo with my friend.

3 The cow is in the shed and three little pigs ——— in the yard.

4 I wore nappies when I ——— a baby.

5 Tomorrow I am ——— to play in the park.

6 Last year I ——— out of a tree and hurt my leg.

7 When I was three I ——— a toy bear.

8 My dog chased me and I ——— as fast as I could.

9 I lost my shoes but then I ——— them in the bin.

From: *Spotlight on Writing*, Routledge © Glynis Hannell 2009

Activity 7

Repairing sentences (1)

LEVEL 2

There is a word missing in each sentence. Write the sentence out again and fill in the missing word.

1   Tomorrow I —— be at school until four o'clock.

2   When I was little I —— milk from a yellow cup.

3   I was —— up in the middle of the night by a loud noise.

4   Today I will swim in the pool, but yesterday I —— in the sea.

5   Yesterday I made a cake, and today I might —— a pie.

6   I fed the pony yesterday and Susan will —— the pony tomorrow.

7   I did not want my sister to see my surprise so I —— it under my bed.

8   Polly said she would send one present but she —— two.

9   The jewels were —— by a thief.

Activity 7

Repairing sentences (1)

LEVEL 3

There is a word missing in each sentence. Write the sentence out again and fill in the missing word.

1 My cousin has caught a cold, I hope I don't —— it too.

2 I —— the black horse as fast as I could to reach the town before night.

3 We watched sunrise, and after the sun had —— we started our journey.

4 The coach driver started at dawn and —— all day.

5 The plant is growing so fast, it has already —— as tall as the fence.

6 The teacher will speak to you next; she has already —— to the other class.

7 I might learn how to keep bees; my uncle —— bees when he was a kid.

8 I will bring a blanket; Tom has already —— a big tent and some chairs.

9 We are all going home. I will leave later today, and my sister —— yesterday.

From: *Spotlight on Writing*, Routledge © Glynis Hannell 2009

Activity 8: Repairing sentences (2)

Teaching notes

In *Repairing sentences (2)* the pupils have to find two words that will fit into the sentence. The task of filling in two words is far more challenging than finding one word. Pupils will need to combine various parts of speech, such as verbs and prepositions, to complete the sentences. Copying the complete sentence out will build the pupils' familiarity with these new structures. This activity really challenges the pupils' ability to work with word order and sentence construction. Teacher input and support will be important in maximising the benefit that pupils derive from this activity.

There may be several appropriate answers. Here are some suggestions. Discuss the options with your pupils to help develop their ability to see the possibilities in sentence construction.

Level 1

1 jumped over, climbed on, ran into
2 live in, come from
3 and cows, who live
4 will get, may get
5 water them
6 care for, look after
7 made from, built of

8 make me, make people
9 I like, I love, I hate

Level 2

1 towards the, around their
2 cared for, fed often, kept warm
3 often fight, are pets, like food
4 the sea, the ocean, the lake
5 My mother, My father, The babysitter
6 I often, you can
7 very dangerous, taught tricks
8 biggest animals, largest creatures
9 straw and, grass or

Level 3

1 lived long, died long
2 should always, need to
3 more person, heavy box, small hole
4 look carefully
5 you should, I always
6 come out, wake up
7 someone wants
8 run as
9 have enough, have any

Activity 8

Repairing sentences (2)

LEVEL 1

There are two words missing in each sentence. Write the sentence out again and fill in the missing words.

1 The little dog —— —— the wall.

2 Giraffes are animals that —— —— Africa.

3 A farmer looks after the pigs —— —— on a farm.

4 If it rains I —— —— wet.

5 Plants will die if you do not —— ——.

6 Mother cats —— —— their kittens.

7 Houses can be —— —— wood.

8 Cartoons —— —— laugh.

9 —— —— to eat peanut butter on toast.

Activity 8

Repairing sentences (2)

LEVEL 2

There are two words missing in each sentence. Write the sentence out again and fill in the missing words.

1 The soldiers marched —— —— castle.

2 Babies need to be —— ——.

3 Cats and dogs —— ——.

4 Boats can go on the river or —— ——.

5 —— —— never lets me stay up late.

6 On the beach —— —— swim or collect shells.

7 Tigers can be —— ——.

8 Whales are the —— —— in the world.

9 Cows eat —— —— hay.

Activity 8

Repairing sentences (2)

LEVEL 3

There are two words missing in each sentence. Write the sentence out again and fill in the missing words.

1 Dinosaurs —— —— ago.

2 When you go shopping you —— —— take some money.

3 One —— —— will make the boat sink.

4 You have to —— —— before you cross the road.

5 In cold weather —— —— wrap up in warm clothes.

6 Nocturnal animals —— —— at night.

7 If the phone rings you know that —— —— to speak to you.

8 In a race you have to —— —— fast as you can.

9 Very poor people do not —— —— money.

From: *Spotlight on Writing*, Routledge © Glynis Hannell 2009

CHAPTER 4

Writing facts and information

Sequence and clarity

Factual writing has its own style and set of conventions. In factual reports, letters and so on the writer needs to be able to:

- provide information clearly and unambiguously;
- organise information into a logical sequence;
- eliminate irrelevant information.

In *Step by step* (Activity 9) pupils have to describe logical sequences of action. This will help pupils learn how to think sequentially. The activity can form the basis of a good class brainstorming session in which pupils work together to make sure that every step is included in the right place. Those pupils who do not find it easy to think in a step-by-step way will be helped by hearing how some of their peers can sequence their ideas, using verbal markers such as *first*, *then*, *after that*, *before*, *at the end* and so on.

In *All they need to know* (Activity 10) the pupils need to be able to write with another person's perspective in mind, making allowance for the fact that their reader (an alien) will know nothing at all about the topic. For some pupils the ability to take on another perspective can be difficult and in this activity the teacher can highlight the need to think about what the other person already knows and what they need to be told.

In *Compare and contrast* (Activity 11) the pupils will need to use words exactly, to give precise explanations of how pairs of words relate to each other. Once again, this is a good activity to introduce first as a class discussion, as all pupils will be able to contribute and be included. The less able pupils will really benefit from seeing how ideas can be refined and clarified, while the more able pupils will be extended and, with teacher guidance, will further develop their thinking and language skills. In turn, this translates to improvements in writing.

Finally, this chapter provides an activity to promote your pupils' skills in telling the difference between factual and opinion writing. In *Fact or opinion?* (Activity 12) pupils are asked to read series of short statements and decide whether each is an opinion or a statement of fact. Although not often taught as a specific skill, grasping the difference between a stated opinion and a stated fact is a very useful skill, enabling pupils to become more discriminating listeners and readers and more accurate writers.

Activity 9: Step by step

Teaching notes

Some types of writing, such as instructions or factual accounts of a temporal nature, need to follow a very clear sequence of steps.

In *Step by step* your pupils are asked to prepare a writing plan. This could be in the form of a flow chart, a sequence of numbered dot points, headings or short sentences or a variety of other alternatives. In some of the activities a time sheet or diary sheet might be a useful way to organise the information.

It is useful to brainstorm the methods that could be used for a writing plan with your class. You may find that you can revisit previous lessons that you have given in planning writing and also introduce new strategies. Encourage the pupils to think of what is the best way to set out the writing plan.

Teachers may find it useful to set small groups of pupils to working collaboratively, each contributing his or her own ideas and negotiating to get the sequence of ideas into shape. All ability levels can be included and contribute, perhaps with the teacher acting as group facilitator.

You may like to get the pupils to follow through and actually use their writing plan as the basis for a completed piece of written work.

Look for a clear and logical sequence of steps. Many pupils tend to leave out important beginning and ending points, so encourage them to include the entire sequence, from start to finish.

You can work out a checklist with your pupils to help them self-monitor their writing plan. Here is an example of a simple checklist.

Necessary features	Yes
Is there a clear starting point? (For example, **Phone vet . . .**)	
Is every step included?	
Are the steps in a logical sequence?	
Are possible variations considered? (For example, **Washing machine/ no washing machine**, when planning how to wash dirty clothes)	
Is there a clear end point? (For example, **Pour baby's bathwater away**)	

Activity 9

Step by step

LEVEL 1

Make a writing plan for each of these. Write down all the things that you have to do and put them in the correct order.

1 How to get ready for bed.

2 A day in the life of a teacher.

3 How to clean your teeth.

4 How to plant a tree.

5 How to wrap a present.

6 How to make a glass of milkshake or cordial.

7 How to wash a dog.

8 How to buy a book.

9 How to make a sandcastle.

Activity 9

Step by step

LEVEL 2

Make a writing plan for each of these. Write down all the things that you have to do and put them in the correct order.

1 How to go on a journey by train.

2 A day in the life of a bus driver.

3 How to find out what the word **ogre** means.

4 How to look after a friend who has grazed their knee.

5 How to send a letter to an aunt who lives in another country.

6 How to find out what is on TV tonight.

7 How to invite a friend over to play.

8 How to buy some new shoes.

9 How to bath a baby.

From: *Spotlight on Writing*, Routledge © Glynis Hannell 2009

Activity 9

Step by step

LEVEL 3

Make a writing plan for each of these. Write down all the things that you have to do and put them in the correct order.

1 How to organise a sports day at school.

2 A day in the life of a deep sea diver.

3 How to put your clock right after it has stopped.

4 How to wash your dirty clothes and get them ready to wear.

5 How to find out the time of the next train at the station.

6 How to arrange for a surprise party for your brother.

7 How to buy a goldfish.

8 How to make a nesting box for wild birds.

9 How to get ready to leave for a camping trip.

Activity 10: All they need to know

Teaching notes

Organising information is an important part of skilled writing. Facts need to be assembled into a structure that the reader can follow logically from one fact to another. Similar facts are grouped together, and groups of ideas are placed in a sequence that makes sense. However, the writer also has to take into account their readers' background knowledge and particular needs. In *All they need to know* the pupils have to imagine that they are giving information to an alien, who will have no prior knowledge of the topic.

The pupils are then asked to draw a plan of what they will tell the alien to make sure they have covered everything the alien needs to know. After that, the pupils are then asked to write down the information, using their plan to organise their ideas.

Brainstorming how to tackle one of the topics can be a very useful class activity. Suggest a topic and then ask for facts about that topic from the pupils. All pupils will be able to make a contribution: some will suggest very obvious, concrete pieces of information that may otherwise be overlooked, while other pupils will think of more abstract information that helps to complete the picture.

At first you will have a collection of random ideas written on the board. Then work with the pupils to show how the ideas can be grouped together and organised to make a coherent piece of written information. You may find that some obvious pieces of information are missing, such as *Elephants are animals*, because the pupils take this information for granted and forget that the 'alien' starts with zero knowledge.

Mind maps, diagrams, paragraph plans, flow charts and various other devices can be used to help organise information into a workable structure. Using such strategies helps all your pupils to understand how to work in a logical way in planning a piece of written work.

Encourage the pupils to ask questions themselves, such as:

- *What sort of thing is it? For example, Is it an animal? Is it a plant? Is it a tool?*

- *What does it look like? For example, How large is it? What shape is it? What colour is it?*

- *Where would you find it?*

- *Does it move? How does it move?*

- *It is useful? Why?*

- *What is it made of? How is it made?*

- *What is special or interesting about it?*

Activity 10

All they need to know

LEVEL 1

Imagine that an alien has come from another planet. The alien asks you to tell them as much as you can about these topics. Draw a plan of what you will tell them to make sure you have covered everything. Then write down your information.

1 frogs

2 schools

3 elephants

4 cookies

5 television

6 farmers

7 vegetables

8 shoes

9 saucepans

Activity 10

All they need to know

LEVEL 2

Imagine that an alien has come from another planet. The alien asks you to tell them as much as you can about these topics. Draw a plan of what you will tell them to make sure you have covered everything. Then write down your information.

1 zoos

2 airports

3 wheels

4 medicine

5 water

6 hats

7 clocks

8 bicycles

9 trumpets

From: *Spotlight on Writing*, Routledge © Glynis Hannell 2009

Activity 10

All they need to know

LEVEL 3

Imagine that an alien has come from another planet. The alien asks you to tell them as much as you can about these topics. Draw a plan of what you will tell them to make sure you have covered everything. Then write down your information.

1 sharks

2 pencils

3 doctors

4 bricks

5 shops

6 rivers

7 influenza

8 speedboats

9 human beings

Activity 11: Compare and contrast

Teaching notes

Thinking about the similarities and differences between two words is a good exercise. Concept development is an important part of language and learning, and being able to isolate the common characteristics and points of difference between two words will, in itself, be a very useful activity for your pupils. However, this can also extend into a very useful and challenging writing activity.

Pupils need very good control over word use and sentence structure in order to be able to complete *Compare and contrast* successfully. The main challenge is in connecting facts to demonstrate how words are alike and then in switching things around to show how the two things differ. Explanations have to be very clear to make sense of what the writer is trying to say.

Work with your pupils to explore the best way to explain the similarities and differences between the words. Encourage the careful selection of words to make meaning as precise as possible. Some pupils may need you to segment the task into two sections, first by working on similarities alone and, when these are complete, going back and working on differences. This helps to clarify the task and make it somewhat easier.

When writing about the similarities between the two words you can encourage the pupils to develop their skills in using words such as *similar, both, the same, the link between* or *alike*. You can also foster the pupils' use of category names, for example *They are both animals* or *They are the same because they are furniture.*

When the pupils have to write about differences between words, this will involve writing about comparisons. For example, pupils may need to include a qualifying word such as *although* or *but*: *One has a flame and one has a bulb, although they both give you light* or *They are both birds but chickens do not fly.*

Writing about differences will also involve the use of comparatives or superlatives. For example, pupils may write *Shoes are stronger than socks* or *Mountains are the highest landforms.*

The pupils may also need to handle negatives as they write about the differences between two words, for example *Crocodiles are dangerous animals, but frogs are not usually dangerous to human beings.*

This activity can generate very valuable classroom discussion and really help to develop all the pupils skills in using words with precision.

There are no teacher's charts for this activity.

Activity 11

Compare and contrast

LEVEL 1

Look at these pairs of words. Explain how these things are alike <u>and</u> how they are different.

1 chicken   seagull

2 shoes   socks

3 snow   rain

4 candle   torch

5 eyelash   eyebrow

6 turn   spin

7 crocodile   frog

8 cheese   yoghurt

9 umbrella   raincoat

Activity 11

Compare and contrast

LEVEL 2

Look at these pairs of words. Explain how these things are alike <u>and</u> how they are different.

1 hands   paws

2 chair   stool

3 plate   dish

4 mountain   hill

5 string   rope

6 bounce   jump

7 town   city

8 tower   lighthouse

9 warm   hot

Activity 11

Compare and contrast

LEVEL 3

Look at these pairs of words. Explain how these things are alike <u>and</u> how they are different.

1 giant ogre

2 knee knuckle

3 mime act

4 sigh cough

5 feast meal

6 bought sold

7 read write

8 bridge tunnel

9 race chase

Activity 12: Fact or opinion?

Teaching notes

Many inexperienced writers tend to write opinion as if it is proven fact and do not understand the difference between the two types of information. One important element in writing is to be aware of whether you are writing proven facts or expressing an opinion. Younger or less able pupils often find it difficult to think objectively about their own thinking in this way. *Fact or opinion?* will help them to understand that difference.

Explain to the pupils that a *fact* is something that everyone would *know* was true. An *opinion* is something that some people *think* or *feel*, but it might not be true and not everyone would agree. Encourage discussion about how the facts could be proved. This is a good introduction to factual writing. Also encourage discussion about how opinions could vary, as this is a good introduction to opinion writing.

Here are the teacher's charts of answers.

Level 1		Level 2		Level 3	
1	THINK	1	KNOW	1	KNOW
2	KNOW	2	THINK	2	THINK
3	THINK	3	THINK	3	THINK
4	THINK	4	KNOW	4	KNOW
5	KNOW	5	KNOW	5	THINK
6	KNOW	6	THINK	6	KNOW
7	THINK	7	KNOW	7	THINK
8	THINK	8	THINK	8	THINK
9	KNOW	9	KNOW	9	KNOW

Activity 12

Fact or opinion?

LEVEL 1

Look at these statements. If the statement is a true fact underline **KNOW**. If the statement is an opinion underline **THINK**.

1 All dogs are cute.   THINK   KNOW

2 Ice is cold.   THINK   KNOW

3 Chocolate is delicious.   THINK   KNOW

4 Yellow socks look weird.   THINK   KNOW

5 Baby pigs are called piglets.   THINK   KNOW

6 Children go to school.   THINK   KNOW

7 Basketball is the best game.   THINK   KNOW

8 Chickens are friendly.   THINK   KNOW

9 Ducks can swim.   THINK   KNOW

Activity 12

Fact or opinion?

LEVEL 2

Look at these statements. If the statement is a true fact underline **KNOW**. If the statement is an opinion underline **THINK**.

1	Elephants live in Africa.	THINK	KNOW
2	Cats are better pets than dogs.	THINK	KNOW
3	Cheese biscuits are great.	THINK	KNOW
4	China cups can sometimes break.	THINK	KNOW
5	Some dogs wear collars.	THINK	KNOW
6	Goldfish are boring pets.	THINK	KNOW
7	Birds make nests in trees.	THINK	KNOW
8	Strawberry is the best flavour yoghurt.	THINK	KNOW
9	The sun sets in the west.	THINK	KNOW

From: *Spotlight on Writing*, Routledge © Glynis Hannell 2009

Activity 12

Fact or opinion?

LEVEL 3

Look at these statements. If the statement is a true fact underline **KNOW**. If the statement is an opinion underline **THINK**.

1 Coffee comes from coffee beans. THINK KNOW

2 Candlelight is better than electric light. THINK KNOW

3 It is not fair to get a medal if you lose a race. THINK KNOW

4 The planets circle the sun. THINK KNOW

5 It is good to read comics. THINK KNOW

6 Shoes are sometimes made of leather. THINK KNOW

7 Spinach tastes good. THINK KNOW

8 The worst weather is when it rains. THINK KNOW

9 Exercise helps you to keep fit. THINK KNOW

CHAPTER 5

Creative writing

Ideas and imagery

How often do teachers hear '*But I don't know what to write*'? The activities in this chapter will help to stimulate ideas and give all pupils a good starting point for interesting, imaginative writing.

Throughout the chapter you will notice that classroom *discussion* and *brainstorming* are suggested as a beginning point to the activities. Why is this?

Pupils vary in their capacity to think creatively and to use their imaginations. Having a group exchange is a good way to stimulate creative ideas. The pupils who already find it easy will find even more new ideas emerging as their fellow pupils share their thoughts. Pupils who tend to think in a concrete, non-imaginative way will also benefit from the class discussion, because this will help to trigger their own imaginations.

Many pupils are at their most comfortable with closed questions (which have 'right' or 'wrong' answers). Open-ended tasks that need a novel and creative response can make these pupils feel very uncomfortable. Classroom discussion can provide these pupils with good role models for creative, 'anything goes' thinking. It also encourages

them to break away from anxiety that what they plan to write sounds 'silly'. As the teacher encourages and values a wide range of ideas and suggestions, these pupils will come to understand that there are often many equally appropriate ways to respond to creative tasks.

In this chapter the pupils have several opportunities to pick up a situation and develop it into an interesting story. For example, in *Keep writing* (Activity 13) pupils are given the beginning of a sentence and asked to continue writing to turn this fragment of a sentence into a story.

In *Use these words* (Activity 14) pupils are asked to build a story around a set of words. The words given provide a 'skeleton' on which pupils can build ideas for a story. In *Mystery and adventure* (Activity 15) pupils are given a summary of a situation and asked to write a story around this idea.

Creative writing also requires interesting and sometimes unusual choices of images and words. In the final activity of this chapter, *Similes* (Activity 16) pupils are asked to create similes of their own. Many pupils never think of using similes in their own creative writing, but it is a simple technique to develop through explicit practice.

Activity 13: Keep writing

Teaching notes

Many pupils find it difficult to think of creative, imaginative ideas or to visualise a scene and develop a storyline from this. The sentences in *Keep writing* give every pupil a flying start by setting an interesting scene and triggering some visualisation.

Using 'what if' thinking is a significant challenge for some pupils. These sentence starters prompt pupils to think '*What will happen next?*', which can then lead to imaginative, creative thinking.

Work with your pupils to encourage them to visualise the scene and predict what might happen next. Brainstorm before the pupils start to write. Prompt them with questions as in the three examples below:

- **Mike looked into the pet shop window and saw . . .**

  Teacher:

  Imagine you are looking in the petshop window yourself. What could you see? Could Mike have seen something really unusual? What do you think Mike will do next?

  Pupils might suggest something like:

  You could see snakes and tortoises . . . there might be a monkey . . . or a kitten . . . Mike could get the monkey and take it home.

- **The eagle swooped down and picked Bertie up in its talons . . .**

  Teacher:

  Just imagine that you are Bertie, the eagle has swooped on you and you are suddenly lifted high in the air! What would it feel like? What would you see? What would happen next?

  Pupils might suggest something like:

  It would feel like flying . . . you could see everything below you . . . like your house getting smaller and smaller . . . and then the eagle might take you to its nest on the mountain top.

- **They peered into the dark cave and saw . . .**

  Teacher:

  Just think about looking into that dark cave. Can you hear or smell anything? What can you see? Could someone or something already be in there?

  Pupils might suggest something like:

  It smells like an animal has been there . . . you could see something shining in the dark . . . there could be a wolf or a bear inside.

Activity 13

Keep writing

LEVEL 1

Finish the sentence. Then write the rest of the story.

1 Mike looked into the pet shop window and saw . . .

2 Mum got the picnic ready and then . . .

3 The lion cub ran, looking for its mother . . .

4 Just as they were all falling asleep they heard a . . .

5 The two monkeys climbed up the . . .

6 Just as they reached the top of the hill a huge . . .

7 The carrot just grew and grew and grew until . . .

8 The wolf smiled sweetly at the hen and said . . .

9 'Help, help!' cried Kelly. 'I am stuck in . . .

From: *Spotlight on Writing*, Routledge © Glynis Hannell 2009

Activity 13

Keep writing

LEVEL 2

Finish the sentence. Then write the rest of the story.

1 The farm gate was wide open and . . .

2 The teacher looked very stern. 'I have just found out that . . .'

3 Becky was amazed when she opened the door. There stood . . .

4 The frog and the snake stared at each other, then suddenly . . .

5 The eagle swooped down and picked Bertie up in its talons . . .

6 Little Georgie was crying very loudly because . . .

7 It was no good, there was no way out. The children were . . .

8 They had never seen anything so funny; there was . . .

9 The king commanded that all the people should . . .

Activity 13

Keep writing

LEVEL 3

Finish the sentence. Then write the rest of the story.

1   It was already getting dark as they rowed towards the shore . . .

2   Father was very angry because George had . . .

3   They peered into the dark cave and saw . . .

4   The helicopter hovered over the roof and then . . .

5   The shark swam swiftly through the water looking for . . .

6   Suddenly there was the sound of trumpets and . . .

7   As they came nearer they could see that the boat was . . .

8   'Come here little goat,' said the crocodile. 'Let me . . .

9   More and more people marched over the bridge until . . .

From: *Spotlight on Writing*, Routledge © Glynis Hannell 2009

Activity 14: Use these words

Teaching notes

Writing a connected story is quite a challenge. Many pupils start with one good idea. For instance, they might decide '*I'll write about a mermaid*,' but then may get stuck and have trouble generating a storyline.

In *Use these words* pupils are given a framework of words that will help to develop a storyline. This task is challenging for younger and less able pupils, so classroom discussion and some individual support may be needed to produce the best responses from pupils who may find it difficult to generate creative ideas or work with language. Level 1 has fewer words to make the task easier.

Talking before writing really helps to generate ideas. Ask questions to start the pupils thinking about possible storylines that incorporate all the words into a story. For example:

- **bee hive stealing honey bear**

  Teacher:

  What is a beehive? What do the bees make in the hive? How come a bear gets into the story. What could happen in a story about a bear and some honey?'

  Pupils might suggest something like:

  A beehive is where the bees make honey . . . they have honeycombs and bring the nectar back from the flowers . . . some bears loves honey . . . they put their paws in the hive if they can . . . but in the story they might get stung.

- **sea mermaid parrot-fish shark cave**

  Teacher:

  Where is this story happening? What could happen if a shark and a mermaid met? What about parrot-fish; who would the parrot-fish be friends with? How does the cave come into the story?

  Pupils might suggest something like:

  It has to be in the sea and it's all about sea creatures . . . sharks would be enemies of mermaids, but parrot-fish would try to protect the mermaid . . . the cave could be a safe place for the mermaid.

- **rocks beware lighthouse storm crash**

  Teacher:

  Do you think this could be an adventure story or a funny story? What is a lighthouse used for? How does it come into this story? What do you think happened? Why was there a crash?

  Pupils might suggest something like:

  It's an adventure story about a shipwreck . . . the lighthouse is supposed to warn the ships of the rocks . . . but maybe it went wrong . . . the crash might be the waves, or the ship on the rocks.

Activity 14

Use these words

LEVEL 1

Write a story and include all the words in a set.
The words can be in any order.

1	grandmother	pet	dog	asleep
2	beach	holiday	played	shells
3	tree	monkey	tricks	banana
4	forest	wolf	scared	ran
5	farm	ducks	farmer	fox
6	bee	hive	honey	bear
7	pig	mud	run	find
8	lost	forest	children	dark
9	twins	train	boots	visit

From: *Spotlight on Writing*, Routledge © Glynis Hannell 2009

Activity 14

Use these words

Write a story and include all the words in a set. The words can be in any order.

1	dog	doughnut	shopkeeper	chased	delicious
2	tree	owl	secret	girl	hidden
3	sea	mermaid	parrot-fish	shark	cave
4	lion	Africa	king	hunter	saved
5	rat	tree	leaves	hidden	shadow
6	thin	stolen	bread	king	showed
7	hand	rope	river	scared	again
8	bear	forest	tracks	turn	claws
9	camel	sand	tent	sun	lost

Activity 14

Use these words

LEVEL 3

Write a story and include all the words in a set. The words can be in any order.

1	sun	pyramid	pharaoh	tomb	river
2	rocks	beware	lighthouse	storm	crash
3	king	amazed	castle	dark	walls
4	desert	camel	tent	afraid	home
5	guitar	wandered	begged	famous	music
6	howl	sled	freezing	tracks	mist
7	truck	chased	disguised	police	siren
8	camp	mountain	avalanche	tumbled	searched
9	alarm	creatures	hunter	together	warning

Activity 15: Mystery and adventure

Teaching notes

Many pupils love to read stories of mystery and adventure. However, some pupils find it very hard to come up with ideas for their own stories. Pupils may simply retell a story that they have read, or recount something that they have seen as a cartoon or adventure movie.

Mystery and adventure helps all the pupils to get started on a story by providing them with a one-line summary of the main idea. Often this is all that is needed to stimulate imaginative ideas and a storyline.

You will find that skilled questioning by the teacher can really help to get the pupils started on developing an interesting and exciting story. Here are some examples of the sorts of questions that you could use:

- **You are given a magic spell that can turn you into a bee.**

  Teacher:

  – How would the spell work? Would it be like a magic word? Or would it be something like clicking your fingers?

  – How would you use it?

  – Could you turn yourself back into a person? How?

  – What would it feel like to turn into a bee?

  – What could you do if you were a bee that you cannot do now?

  – What things would be impossible to do if you were a bee?

  – What adventures could you have if you were a bee?

- **Your pet cat is trapped in a cage. The key is in a giant's pocket.**

  Teacher:

  – How did the cat get into the cage?

  – What sort of cat is it? Is it a shy cat, or maybe it is a brave, strong sort of cat?

  – How do you know the key is in the giant's pocket?

  – What ways can you think of to get the key and rescue the cat?

  – How will the giant try to stop you?

  – How will you succeed?

- **You discover a secret map that leads to treasure.**

  Teacher:

  – How do you discover the map?

  – Are you by yourself or is someone else going to be in the story too?

  – What is shown on the map? Does it look dangerous?

  – What happens when you follow the map?

  – Do you find the treasure?

  – What happens next?

Activity 15

Mystery and adventure

LEVEL 1

Write a story about one of these topics.

1 There is a loud knocking on your window.

2 You find a dinosaur in your garden.

3 You are sitting on the carpet. It gives a shake and flies into the air.

4 Your cat grows to the size of a horse.

5 You and your friend wake up on a desert island.

6 You are given a magic spell that can turn you into a bee.

7 There is a weird green light coming from your fridge.

8 Your dog has to rescue you from a gang of bullies.

9 Your teacher turns into a polar bear.

From: *Spotlight on Writing*, Routledge © Glynis Hannell 2009

Activity 15

Mystery and adventure

LEVEL 2

Write a story about one of these topics.

1 You find a hidden room under an old house.

2 A time machine takes you forward into the next century.

3 You overhear robbers planning to steal your neighbour's dog.

4 If you sit in a special chair you can travel wherever you like.

5 Your pet cat is trapped in a cage. The key is in a giant's pocket.

6 You rescue two children who have fallen into a swamp.

7 You become lost in a huge jungle where wild animals roam.

8 You discover a magic shell that makes your wishes come true.

9 Your mirror shows you what will happen in the future.

Activity 15

Mystery and adventure

LEVEL 3

Write a story about one of these topics.

1 You are accidentally locked in the space shuttle just before take-off.

2 You are kidnapped by a pirate ship.

3 A time machine takes you back in history.

4 There seems to be an invisible hand moving things in your room.

5 You are a cabin boy on a sailing ship. The ship is wrecked in a storm.

6 You discover a secret map that leads to treasure.

7 You become lost in an underground passage deep underground.

8 You see a man fall down a cliff and help to rescue him.

9 Your dog leads you to a mysterious and deserted house.

Activity 16: Similes

Teaching notes

Pupils do not always think of using similes in their own writing. However, they are a good way to add interest and originality to a piece of writing. In *Similes* the pupils have to focus on creating their own. Encourage interesting and unusual ideas.

There are many possible responses, but here are some suggestions.

Level 1

1   a tomato, a strawberry, a fire truck

2   a canoe, a bucket, a matchbox

3   glittering gold, silver dust, a soft pillow

4   a folded blanket, a shadow, a thief

5   a tree, a giant, a lamppost

6   a bird's nest, a carpet of prickles, a pile of wool

7   a doughnut, a piglet, a feather cushion

8   a lion, ten dogs, an eagle

9   a bunch of flowers, a paintbox, the inside of a shell

Level 2

1   my blanket, a jewel, the ocean

2   a racehorse, a greyhound, an Olympic winner

3   soap, silk, ice

4   mouldy bread, bat's blood, old socks

5   a cookie in the oven, boiling water, a sunbeam

6   marshmallow, fresh bread, a pile of hay

7   tyres screeching, chalk on a board, murder

8   a potato, a cookie, my hand

9   jumping over a flea, scratching my nose, blinking

Level 3

1   sandpaper, a cactus, tyres on gravel

2   a beer bottle, mouldy potatoes, a grave

3   a fly in a jar, a cat in a box, a kite in a storm

4   a volcano, a thunderstorm, a tornado

5   a trumpet, a bear, a silver bell

6   birds in a tree, monkeys, castanets

7   a dolphin, a pebble, a bubble

8   paper, a lily, a slice of bread

9   a waterfall, silk ribbons, a tidal wave

Activity 16

Similes

LEVEL 1

Complete these phrases to make them interesting.

1 Her face was as red as . . .

2 Her shoe was as big as . . .

3 The sand was like . . .

4 The cat was as quiet as . . .

5 Joe was as tall as . . .

6 Her hair looked like . . .

7 The puppy was fatter than . . .

8 Sasha was as brave as . . .

9 The colours were like . . .

From: *Spotlight on Writing*, Routledge © Glynis Hannell 2009

Activity 16

Similes

LEVEL 2

Complete these phrases to make them interesting.

1 The sky is as blue as . . .

2 Robert ran like . . .

3 The pavement is as slippery as . . .

4 The taste was worse than . . .

5 I'm as hot as . . .

6 The bed was as soft as . . .

7 The cats' singing sounded like . . .

8 The hole in her sock was bigger than . . .

9 It was as easy as . . .

Activity 16

Similes

LEVEL 3

Complete these phrases to make them interesting.

1 His voice was as rough as . . .

2 The cellar smelled like . . .

3 Todd was behaving crazier than . . .

4 His temper was like . . .

5 Last night she sang like . . .

6 The children chattered as if they were . . .

7 In the water she was just like . . .

8 She was as pale as . . .

9 The rain fell like . . .

From: *Spotlight on Writing*, Routledge © Glynis Hannell 2009

CHAPTER 6

Writing fluency

From thoughts into words

In order to be able to participate fully in the classroom programme, pupils have to be able to write fluently. However, younger or less able writers frequently have trouble in getting their ideas down on paper and this can significantly disadvantage them. There are two main reasons for a lack of writing fluency.

First, there can be difficulties with the production of the actual language and ideas that are the essential foundations for any writing. Throughout this book you will find activities designed to promote your pupils' ability to generate ideas, formulate sentences and organise written language. Without a rapid and easy flow of language and ideas, pupils will be unable to write smoothly and at speed.

Second, there can be difficulties with the process of transferring language into a physical, written form. Even when pupils can generate ideas and language fluently they may still experience difficulties in 'getting their ideas down on paper'.

The skill of transferring internal thoughts and language on to paper through the physical act of writing takes time and practice to develop. A pupil's ideas and words may run ahead of physical writing or typing, so that the pupil is constantly trying to catch up. Sometimes the pupil may be so anxious about accurate spelling and punctuation that they frequently hesitate as they write. In these circumstances the pupil may lose track of their ideas and fluency is lost.

In *Write this down!* (Activity 17) pupils are given short phrases to write down. Learning to write in phrases, rather than word by word, is an important skill that is developed in these dictation exercises. In *Broken sentences* (Activity 18) the pupils have to write dictated sentences quickly using a framework of keywords. In *Writing dash* (Activity 19) the pupils are encouraged to write fluently, getting a first draft down quickly and confidently without worrying too much about spelling or punctuation.

The activities in this chapter will help to build your pupils' abilities to make that important link between their ideas, their language and their physical written output. Although it is probable that most pupils will use handwriting to complete these activities, there is no reason why typing practice cannot also be given using the same learning materials.

Activity 17: Write this down

Teaching notes

Pupils' writing may be slow or stilted because they are afraid of making mistakes. To write fluently, pupils have to be confident, versatile and inventive. In this activity the pupils have to write down phrases as quickly as they can, to rehearse the skill of 'having a go' at whatever words or phrases are needed. Accuracy is not important; quick approximations are quite acceptable for the purpose of this activity.

On the worksheets the pupils are then told just to have a guess if they are not sure about how to spell a word. They can look at the groups of words first, but must cover them up when they write.

You may prefer not to let your pupils see the words before they begin to write. If so, simply omit the last two sentences of the instructions on the worksheets and give pupils a blank sheet of paper to write on.

Here are the teacher's charts of phrases.

Level 1

1   my blue pen
2   a small car
3   the funny boy
4   one big balloon
5   two little ducks
6   running fast
7   his own carriage
8   a huge surprise
9   so many people

Level 2

1   a dazzling light
2   the gloomy cave
3   a loud explosion
4   her special place
5   a smelly goat
6   the stolen treasure
7   a lonely pelican
8   the emergency stop
9   huge feather pillow

Level 3

1   a terrible shriek
2   sleeping soundly
3   the largest ship
4   the most amazing sight
5   my favourite aunt
6   thousands of invaders
7   the ancient pyramid
8   a mysterious shadow
9   natural environment

Activity 17

Write this down

LEVEL 1

Your teacher will read out some words. Write the words down as quickly as you can. Just have a guess if you are not sure about how to spell a word. You can look at the groups of words first. But cover them up when you write.

1 my blue pen

2 a small car

3 the funny boy

4 one big balloon

5 two little ducks

6 running fast

7 his own carriage

8 a huge surprise

9 so many people

Activity 17

Write this down

LEVEL 2

Your teacher will read out some words. Write the words down as quickly as you can. Just have a guess if you are not sure about how to spell a word. You can look at the groups of words first. But cover them up when you write.

1   a dazzling light

2   the gloomy cave

3   a loud explosion

4   her special place

5   a smelly goat

6   the stolen treasure

7   a lonely pelican

8   the emergency stop

9   huge feather pillow

From: *Spotlight on Writing*, Routledge © Glynis Hannell 2009

Activity 17

Write this down

LEVEL 3

Your teacher will read out some words. Write the words down as quickly as you can. Just have a guess if you are not sure about how to spell a word. You can look at the groups of words first. But cover them up when you write.

1 a terrible shriek

2 sleeping soundly

3 the largest ship

4 the most amazing sight

5 my favourite aunt

6 thousands of invaders

7 the ancient pyramid

8 a mysterious shadow

9 natural environment

Activity 18: Broken sentences

Teaching notes

This activity helps to develop the pupils' ability to 'hold' a sentence in their mind as they write. In the same way that copying notes requires the pupil to read, remember and write, *Broken sentences* builds the link between copying words and remembering sentences. The vocabulary used is challenging and this helps to develop the pupils' familiarity with new words through copying them down.

The teacher reads out the proper sentence while the pupils look at the broken version. Pupils are then told to write the full sentence. They can copy the words as they write the sentence.

Here are the teacher's charts of the completed sentences.

Level 1

1   The wooden horse was lost in the attic.
2   The puppy rolled in the mud.
3   A fly was trapped in a spider's web.
4   Uncle gave Sam a new red bicycle.
5   I saw lots of mice in a nest.
6   I like to drink hot chocolate.
7   Tortoises go to sleep in winter.
8   The firemen put out the fire.
9   Chickens live on farms and lay eggs.

Level 2

1   Jack and his mother bought a present for father.
2   You must beware of wolves in the forest.
3   Bats live in caves and hunt at night.
4   If you jump out of a plane you need a parachute.
5   At the circus you will see clowns and acrobats.
6   If you don't clean your teeth they will decay.
7   When a volcano erupts it throws out ash and hot rocks.
8   The North Pole is covered with snow and ice all year round.
9   An ambulance comes when there has been an accident.

Level 3

1   Icebergs float in the sea after they have broken off from glaciers.
2   A python is a type of large snake called a constrictor.
3   Long ago humans lived in caves and hunted wild animals.
4   The person who wins the most races is called a champion.
5   Your heart pumps blood around your body to keep you alive.
6   A tsunami is a huge wave made by an earthquake.
7   The earth is the third planet from the sun; Mercury and Venus are nearer.
8   The bird-eating tarantula is probably the biggest spider in the world.
9   The sloth is the slowest animal on Earth; it would take a month to walk a mile.

Activity 18

Broken sentences

LEVEL 1

Look at these broken sentences. They have lots of little
words missing. Your teacher will read the proper sentence out
so that you can write it down.

1 —— wooden horse —— lost —— —— attic.

2 —— puppy rolled —— —— mud.

3 —— fly —— trapped —— —— spider's web.

4 Uncle —— Sam —— new —— bicycle.

5 —— —— lots —— mice —— —— nest.

6 —— —— —— drink hot chocolate.

7 Tortoises —— —— sleep —— winter.

8 —— firemen —— out —— fire.

9 Chickens live —— farms —— lay eggs.

Activity 18

Broken sentences

LEVEL 2

Look at these broken sentences. They have lots of little words missing. Your teacher will read the proper sentence out so that you can write it down.

1   Jack —— —— mother bought —— present —— father.

2   —— must beware —— wolves —— —— forest.

3   Bats live —— caves —— hunt —— night.

4   —— —— jump —— —— —— plane —— need —— parachute.

5   —— —— circus —— —— see clowns —— acrobats.

6   —— —— —— clean your teeth —— —— decay.

7   —— —— volcano erupts —— throws —— ash —— ——
    rocks.

8   —— North Pole —— covered —— snow —— ice all year
    round.

9   —— ambulance —— when —— —— —— —— accident.

From: *Spotlight on Writing*, Routledge © Glynis Hannell 2009

Activity 18

Broken sentences

LEVEL 3

Look at these broken sentences. They have lots of little words missing. Your teacher will read the proper sentence out so that you can write it down.

1 Icebergs float —— —— sea after —— —— broken —— —— glaciers.

2 —— python —— —— type —— large —— called —— constrictor.

3 Long ago —— lived —— caves —— —— wild animals.

4 —— person —— wins —— most —— —— called —— champion.

5 —— —— —— blood around —— —— to keep —— ——.

6 —— tsunami —— —— huge —— —— —— —— earthquake.

7 —— earth —— —— —— planet from —— ——; Mercury —— Venus —— ——.

8 —— ——-eating tarantula —— probably the biggest —— —— —— ——.

9 —— sloth —— —— —— —— on earth; —— —— —— —— month to walk a mile.

Activity 19: Writing dash

Teaching notes

Writing dash is a good exercise to develop writing fluency. Writing quickly helps to develop the automatic link between thinking and writing. This activity helps pupils to focus on getting their ideas down, just as they are.

Some pupils may find it difficult to generate ideas of what to write. These pupils will benefit from brainstorming with a group or even the whole class. An open sharing of ideas means that all pupils can contribute and the less confident pupils can see that 'anything goes' as long as it is related to the topic.

Pupils are told to write as much as they can on a topic, as fast as they can until the teacher tells them to stop. They should be told not to worry about spelling or punctuation at this point, as this can be fixed later on.

Here are some teacher's guidelines:

- Set a time limit for each item or for the whole sheet.

- No more than 2 minutes per topic or 15 minutes for the whole sheet is usually about right, depending on the pupils' abilities.

- Pupils should keep writing until told to stop.

- Use a clock or stopwatch to keep track of time.

- Create a sense of urgency, and emphasise the need for speed.

- Maybe do a sample 'writing dash' yourself on the board to show pupils what is required.

- Ask the pupils:
  - to write whatever comes into their heads;
  - to write as fast as they can;
  - to keep writing until told to stop;
  - to write single words if necessary;
  - not to worry about neat handwriting;
  - not to worry about spelling or punctuation.

Activity 19

Writing dash

LEVEL 1

Here are some topics to write about. You have to write as much as you can, as fast as you can. Don't worry about spelling or punctuation right now. You can fix that later. Your teacher will tell you how long you have and when you should stop writing.

1 hands

2 frogs

3 leaves

4 red

5 chickens

6 school

7 farms

8 boats

9 night-time

Activity 19

Writing dash

LEVEL 2

Here are some topics to write about. You have to write as much as you can, as fast as you can. Don't worry about spelling or punctuation right now. You can fix that later. Your teacher will tell you how long you have and when you should stop writing.

1 eggs

2 scissors

3 elephants

4 road signs

5 blue

6 going to sleep

7 refrigerators

8 pancakes

9 summer

Activity 19

Writing dash

LEVEL 3

Here are some topics to write about. You have to write as much as you can, as fast as you can. Don't worry about spelling or punctuation right now. You can fix that later. Your teacher will tell you how long you have and when you should stop writing.

1 eyes

2 lions

3 feathers

4 yellow

5 waking up

6 newspapers

7 telephones

8 clocks

9 winter

CHAPTER 7

Editing

And finally . . .

Many pupils think that, once spelling and punctuation have been checked, their work is edited, polished and complete. However, as professional writers will attest, good editing requires a far greater range of skills than simple proofreading and correction of errors in spelling and punctuation. A piece of writing is not complete until it has also been checked for interesting, appropriate content, skilled use of words, good organisation of ideas, correct grammar and well-structured sentences.

The development of skilled writing is a process that takes many years, perhaps some would say a lifetime! At first, pupils naturally concentrate on the absolute fundamentals of writing, such as forming the letters, getting words down with correct, or reasonably approximate, spelling and making sense to the reader. Gradually their skills develop and they begin to write more, at a greater speed and with more complexity.

As teachers we also look for evidence of emerging craftsmanship in the way our pupils write. Are the pupils becoming critical readers of their own work? Can they discriminate between good and poor written expression? Can they identify problems with the organisation and structure of their own work? Can they recognise and reject repetition? These and other related skills are the components of good writing that we hope our pupils will gradually understand and put into practice.

This chapter gives your pupils the opportunity to edit a range of passages that contain many writing faults. Reading and identifying problems in other people's writing is far easier for the pupils than being critical readers of their own work. However, the skills that are developed will readily flow through to the pupils' own writing. Discussion between pupils and teacher enhances this process and helps the pupils to understand just how to edit a piece of work to eliminate a range of problems and improve the overall quality of the writing.

Editing checklist

- Does this answer the question that was set?

- Does my writing make sense?

- Are all my sentences well structured?

- Have I avoided run-on sentences?

- Have I used the right verb tense and/or form?

- Do I repeat words or ideas unnecessarily?

- Have I left out any words?

- Have I left out any important information?

- Have I included irrelevant information that needs to be edited out?

- Is my writing dull; does it need to be made more interesting?

- Have I used a good range of vocabulary and avoided words that are boring or too general?

- Have I used jargon or slang that needs to be replaced with better words or phrases?

- Have I put the information in the correct sequence?

- Is my work well structured into paragraphs so that it is easy for the reader to follow?

- Do I need to use layout devices such as headings or tables to make my work clearer?

- Is there anything I can do to make this a better piece of writing?

- What do I really like about this work? Can I extend these strengths?

- Have I fixed my spelling mistakes?

- Have I punctuated correctly?

- 'Yes' to all of these? Then I have finished!

Activity 20: You can edit!

Teaching notes for Level 1

Here are the important editing points in this passage, followed by a sample rewrite.

What I did yesterday

i[1] whent[2] to school i[3] whent[4] to the park i[5] whent[6] to the shop i[7] whent[8,9] home. i[10] watched TV it was good i[11] had a shower it was good i[12] had a cookie it was good[13] it tasted of ginger.[14] The end.

Sample rewrite

Yesterday I went to school. After school I played in the park. Then I visited the shop and after that I went home. I watched TV and that was fun. Then I had a shower, and after that I ate a delicious ginger cookie.

1 Capital 'I' needed.
2 Spelling.
3 Capital 'I' needed.
4 Spelling.
5 Capital 'I' needed.
6 Spelling.
7 Capital 'I' needed.
8 Spelling.
9 Fourth repetition of **I went**. Need to rewrite to avoid so many repetitions.
10 Capital 'I' needed.
11 Capital 'I' needed.
12 Capital 'I' needed.
13 Third repetition of **it was good**. Need to rewrite to avoid so many repetitions. Run-on sentence.
14 Good information.

Activity 20

You can edit!

LEVEL 1

Edit and rewrite this passage.

What I did yesterday

i whent to school i whent to the

park i whent to the shop i whent

home. i watched TV it was good

i had a shower it was good i had

a cookie it was good it tasted of

ginger. The end.

Activity 20: You can edit!

Teaching notes for Level 2

Here are the important editing points in this passage, followed by a sample rewrite.

At the circus

At the cicus[1] I saw some clarns[2] and some ladies and some other things.[3] We had to sit on bench things[4] and my legs hert.[5] We laffed[6] and laffed[7] because the clarn[8] fell in the bucket of water.[9] I had a good time.[10]

Sample rewrite

I saw some funny clowns at the circus. I also saw ladies who rode on horses and some acrobats on the high wire. We laughed and laughed because the clown fell in the bucket of water. We had to sit on a bench and that made my legs hurt, but I still had a good time.

---

1 Spelling.
2 Spelling.
3 Lack of interest: **other things** should be named properly.
4 Poor vocabulary: **bench things** could be **benches, wooden seats** or similar.
5 Spelling.
6 Spelling.
7 Spelling.
8 Spelling.
9 Interesting information.
10 Good to finish with a final sentence.

Activity 20

You can edit!

LEVEL 2

Edit and rewrite this passage.

At the circus

At the cicus I saw some clarns and

some ladies and some other things.

We had to sit on bench things and

my legs hert. We laffed and laffed

because the clarn fell in the bucket

of water. I had a good time.

Activity 20: You can edit!

Teaching notes for Level 3

Here are the important editing points in this passage, followed by a sample rewrite.

Elephants in Africa

on[1] monday[2] we go[3] to the libree[4] and we saw a video about africa.[5] the[6] video showed us how the elephants is[7] all looking for food but there is not much food.[8] the[9] big elephants looking[10] after the little elephants. the[11] little elepants[12] are calffs[13] and they is[14] little elephants.[15] The little elephants keeps[16] in the middle of the other elephants to keep safe. Mrs Jones came into the libree[17] and told us a story about baseball[18,19]

Sample rewrite

On Monday we went to the library and saw a video about Africa. The video showed us how the elephants in Africa are searching for food, but there is not enough for them to eat. The young elephants are called calves. We also saw how the older elephants look after the calves and keep them safe in the middle of the herd. [Omit reference to story about baseball as this is irrelevant to the topic.]

1 Capital letter needed.
2 Capital letter needed.
3 Should be **went** not **go**.
4 Spelling.
5 Capital letter needed.
6 Capital letter needed.
7 Should be **are** not **is**.
8 Poor sentence structure in **looking for food but there is not much food**.
9 Capital letter needed.
10 Should be **look** not **looking**.
11 Capital letter needed.
12 Spelling.
13 Spelling.
14 Should be **are** not **is**.
15 Repetition of **little elephants** in **the little elepants are calffs and they is little elephants**.
16 Should be **keep** not **keeps**.
17 Spelling.
18 Irrelevant information for the title of **Elephants in Africa**. Should be deleted.
19 Full stop needed.

Activity 20

You can edit!

LEVEL 3

Edit and rewrite this passage.

Elephants in Africa

on monday we go to the libree and we saw a video about africa. the video showed us how the elephants is all looking for food but there is not much food. the big elephants looking after the little elephants. the little elepants are calffs and they is little elephants. The little elephants keeps in the middle of the other elephants to keep safe. Mrs Jones came into the libree and told us a story about baseball.

Activity 21: Spot the mistakes

Teaching notes for Level 1

Here are the important editing points in this passage, followed by a sample rewrite.

The magic show

On my birthday I[1] a lot of stuff[2] and I liked it.[3] On my birthday my frends[4] came[5] my house and we saw a magic show the magic man[6] made a rabbit come out of a hat I liked that and it was good and I liked it.[7,8] The magic man[9] hid my hat, he hidded[10,11] it and it was gon.[12] And he hidded[13] it behind a certin[14] it[15, 16] was black. I had a good birthday.[17]

Sample rewrite

On my birthday I was given lots of great presents that I liked. My friends came to my house and we saw a magic show. The best part was when the magician pulled a rabbit out of his hat. The magician also made my hat disappear behind a black curtain. So I had a really good birthday.

---

1 Word missing: should be **received**, **was given** or similar.
2 Poor vocabulary: **stuff** is not a good word; **gifts**, **presents**, **treats** or similar would be better.
3 Unclear: **it** could refer to the birthday or it could refer to the **stuff**.
4 Spelling.
5 Word missing: **my friends came to my house**.
6 Poor vocabulary: **magician** is better than **magic man**.
7 Run-on sentence from **On my birthday . . .** through to **. . . and I liked it**.
8 Poor sentence construction with repetition in **I liked that and it was good and I liked it**.
9 Poor vocabulary: **magician** is better than **magic man**.
10 Should be **hid** not **hidded**.
11 Repetition in **hid my hat, he hidded it**.
12 Spelling.
13 Should be **hid** not **hidded**.
14 Spelling.
15 No indication of what **it** refers to. It could be the curtain or the hat.
16 Run-on sentence.
17 Good to have a final sentence.

Activity 21

Spot the mistakes

LEVEL 1

Edit and rewrite this passage.

The magic show

On my birthday I a lot of stuff and I liked it. On my birthday my frends came my house and we saw a magic show the magic man made a rabbit come out of a hat I liked that and it was good and I liked it. The magic man hid my hat, he hidded it and it was gon. And he hidded it behind a certin it was black I had a good birthday.

Activity 21: Spot the mistakes

Teaching notes for Level 2

Here are the important editing points in this passage, followed by a sample rewrite.

My birthday

wen[1,2] it was my brithday[3] my Mum a cake[4] for me and[5] I did not like the cake so[6] I do not like chocolate cake[7] and she said never[8] mind I will make you another cake[9] We went to park[10] on my brithday[11] and it was good[12] we play[13] on the swings and we play[14] on the slippery dip to.[15] Then we went back home and I went to bed and[16] I was seven.

Sample rewrite

Mum baked a cake for my seventh birthday, but I did not like it because it was a chocolate cake. Mum said 'Never mind, I will bake you another one.' After we had the cake we went to the park and played on the swings and the slippery dip. Then we went home and I went to bed.

1 Capital letter needed.
2 Spelling.
3 Spelling.
4 Word missing: should read **Mum made a cake . . ., Mum baked a cake** or similar.
5 Here, **but** would be a better word than **and**.
6 Should be **because**, not **so**.
7 Poor sentence construction: the word **cake** used three times in the same sentence.
8 Speech marks and capital letter needed.

9 Speech marks and full stop needed.
10 Missing word: **We went to the park**.
11 Spelling.
12 Full stop needed, then capital letter.
13 Should be **played** not **play**.
14 Should be **played** not **play**.
15 Should be **too** not **to**.
16 Could have used a full stop and started a new sentence, **I was seven**, or incorporated age in an earlier sentence.

Activity 21

Spot the mistakes

LEVEL 2

Edit and rewrite this passage.

My birthday

wen it was my brithday my Mum a cake for me and I did not like the cake so I do not like chocolate cake and she said never mind I will make you another cake. We went to park on my brithday and it was good we play on the swings and we play on the slippery dip to. Then we went back home and I went to bed and I was seven.

Activity 21: Spot the mistakes

Teaching notes for Level 3

Here are the important editing points in this passage, followed by a sample rewrite.

The surprise

Mum and Dad promised me a surprise for my birthday. I was very excited. I could hardly wait. When the postman came and[1] he had a parcel[2] and he said here[3] is a parcel for you[4] and I said thank[5] you for the parcel[6] and he said[7] its[8,9] all right[10,11] and[12] then I opened the parcel and[13] it was a surpise[14,15] and[16] I said thank[17] you Mum[18] thank you Dad.[19,20] Then we went to my uncles[21] place and we had a party. I had a good birthday.[22]

Sample rewrite

Mum and Dad promised me a surprise for my birthday. I was very excited. I could hardly wait. The postman came with a huge parcel. I thanked him and then I opened the parcel as fast as I could. It was a model aeroplane, which was just what I wanted. 'Thank you very much,' I said to Mum and Dad. Then we went to my uncle's place and had a party. I had had a very good birthday.

1 The word **and** is not needed in this sentence.

2 An adjective would make **a parcel** more interesting, for example **a huge parcel**.

3 Speech marks and capital letter needed.

4 Speech marks and full stop needed.

5 Speech marks and capital letter needed.

6 Speech marks and full stop needed, followed by capital letter.

7 Repetition in **and he said . . . and I said . . . and he said**.

8 Speech marks and capital letter needed.

9 Should be **it's** not **its** as an abbreviation of **it is**.

10 Speech marks and full stop needed.

11 Dull writing: **its all right**.

12 Another repeat of **and**.

13 Another repeat of **and**.

14 Spelling.

15 Dull writing: the writer does not tell the reader what the surprise was.

16 Another repeat of **and**.

17 Speech marks and capital letter needed.

18 Some sort of punctuation needed.

19 Speech marks and full stop needed.

20 Dull writing: **thank you Mum thank you Dad**.

21 Should be **uncles'** (two or more uncles' home) or **uncle's** (one uncle's home).

22 Good to finish with a final sentence.

Activity 21

Spot the mistakes

LEVEL 3

Edit and rewrite this passage.

The surprise

Mum and Dad promised me a surprise for my birthday. I was very excited. I could hardly wait. When the postman came and he had a parcel and he said here is a parcel for you and I said thank you for the parcel and he said its all right and then I opened the parcel and it was a surpise and I said thank you Mum thank you Dad. Then we went to my uncles place and we had a party. I had a good birthday.

Activity 22: Make it better!

Teaching notes for Level 1

Here are the important editing points in this passage, followed by a sample rewrite.

How to make a cheese and ham sandwich

You got to[1] put the bit of bred[2,3] on top of the bit of bred.[4,5,6] Get the bred[7] and get the other stuff.[8] Lots of butter on the bread with a niff.[9,10] Put yor[11] chees[12] and yor[13] tomato[14] on the bred.[15,16] Then you can eat yor[17] sandwich. Very delicious.[18] You have to cut the sandwich[19,20]

Sample rewrite

Gather together the bread and the other ingredients. Use a knife to spread plenty of butter on the bread. Put your cheese and ham on to one piece of bread. Put the other piece of bread on top. Cut the sandwich and then you can eat it. It will be delicious.

1 Poor expression: **you have to** or **you should** would be better.

2 Spelling.

3 Poor expression: **a slice of bread** or **a piece of bread** would be better.

4 Spelling.

5 Poor expression: need to use words such as **the other slice of bread** to show that there are two slices.

6 Putting the two slices of bread together should come later in the process.

7 Spelling.

8 A better word than **stuff** is needed: **ingredients** or **things** might be better.

9 Beginning of sentence needs a pronoun + verb, such as **you spread** or **you have to put**.

10 Spelling.

11 Spelling.

12 Spelling.

13 Spelling.

14 The sandwich was supposed to have **cheese** and **ham** not **tomato**.

15 Spelling.

16 This is where the second slice of bread should be put on top of the first slice.

17 Spelling.

18 **Very delicious** is not a sentence; it should be rewritten with a verb or merged into another sentence.

19 Cutting the sandwich should come before it is eaten.

20 A full stop is needed at the end of this sentence.

Activity 22

Make it better!

LEVEL 1

Edit and rewrite this passage.

How to make a cheese and ham sandwich

You got to put the bit of bred on top of the bit of bred. Get the bred and get the other stuff. Lots of butter on the bread with a niff. Put yor chees and yor tomato on the bred. Then you can eat yor sandwich. Very delicious. You have to cut the sandwich

Activity 22: Make it better!

Teaching notes for Level 2

Here are the important editing points in this passage, followed by a sample rewrite.

Red Riding Hood

The little girl[1] name was Red Riding Hood. Her Mum said You[2] go to grandmother in the wood.[3] Red Riding Hood look[4] at the wolf and he look[5] at Red Riding Hood. War[6,7] are you goin[8,9,10] I[11] am goin[12] to grandmother.[13,14,15] The wolf put on grandmother[16] dress and Red Riding Hood said what[17] big teeth[18] and the wolf jumped out and Red Riding Hood was so terrified[19] that she scrimmed[20] and scrimmed.[21] The wolf runned[22] away and it was all OK.[23]

Sample rewrite

There was a little girl called Red Riding Hood. One day, her Mum said 'Go and see grandmother in the wood.' On the way, Red Riding Hood met a wolf. The wolf asked her 'Where are you going?' 'I am going to grandmother's house,' replied Red Riding Hood, and the wolf went on his way. At her grandmother's house, the wolf put on the old lady's dress and bonnet. When Red Riding Hood arrived, she cried 'What big teeth you have, grandmother!' Then the wolf jumped out of the old lady's clothes. Red Riding Hood was so terrified that she screamed and screamed. Her screams were so loud that the wolf ran away and Red Riding Hood was safe.

1 Should be **girl's** not **girl**.
2 Speech marks needed.
3 Speech marks needed.
4 Should be **looked** not **look**.
5 Should be **looked** not **look**.
6 Speech marks needed.
7 Spelling.
8 Spelling.
9 Needs a question mark and end speech marks.
10 Needs a phrase such as **asked the wolf**.
11 Speech marks needed.
12 Spelling.
13 Speech marks needed.

14 Better to use **grandmother's house** than just **grandmother**.
15 Needs a phrase such as **said Red Riding Hood**.
16 Should be **grandmother's** not **grandmother**.
17 Speech marks and capital letter needed.
18 Speech marks needed: could use an exclamation mark or a full stop.
19 Good word.
20 Spelling incorrect but a good word.
21 Spelling incorrect but a good word.
22 Should be **ran** not **runned**.
23 **OK** should be replaced with a less colloquial phrase.

Activity 22

Make it better!

LEVEL 2

Edit and rewrite this passage.

Red Riding Hood

The little girl name was Red Riding Hood.

Her Mum said You go to grandmother in the

wood. Red Riding Hood look at the wolf and

he look at Red Riding Hood. War are you

goin I am goin to grandmother. The wolf put

on grandmother dress and Red Riding Hood

said what big teeth and the wolf jumped out

and Red Riding Hood was so terrified that she

scrimmed and scrimmed. The wolf runned

away and it was all OK.

Activity 22: Make it better!

Teaching notes for Level 3

Here are the important editing points in this passage, followed by a sample rewrite.

How to make a book

First you have to get enough paper for the book. With[1] the paper it[2] has to be the right paper not to[3] thick not to[4] skinny.[5,6] Covers for the outside.[7] You can decorate[8] with amazing patterns. Cut all the paper[9] and then you have the pages for the book. You have to think how big the book will be too.[10] With[11] all the pages you can use glue or staples[12] and make the book.[13] And[14] then the book is done and you can write in it.

Sample rewrite

First, you have to find enough paper to make a book. It is important that the paper is just the right thickness, not too thin and not too thick. You will also need to find some card for the covers of the book. Once you have decided on the size of the book, you can cut the paper into pages and then glue or staple the pages together. After that you can put the covers on the book. If you like, the covers can be decorated with amazing patterns. The book is then ready for you to write in.

1 **With** is not a good way to begin this sentence.
2 The word **it** is not needed if the sentence is rewritten correctly, for example **The paper has to be . . .**
3 Should be **too** not **to**.
4 Should be **too** not **to**.
5 Should be **thin** not **skinny**.
6 This is a clumsy sentence and needs punctuation. See sample rewrite.
7 This is an incomplete sentence.

8 What can be decorated?
9 You would need to work out the size of the book before you cut the pages.
10 This should come before making the covers or cutting the pages.
11 It is not good to start a sentence with **with**.
12 How are the glue and staples used?
13 There is no mention of the covers here.
14 **And** is not a good way to start a sentence and could be omitted.

Activity 22

Make it better!

LEVEL 3

Edit and rewrite this passage.

How to make a book

First you have to get enough paper for the book. With the paper it has to be the right paper not to thick not to skinny. Covers for the outside. You can decorate with amazing patterns. Cut all the paper and then you have the pages for the book. You have to think how big the book will be too. With all the pages you can use glue or staples and make the book. And then the book is done and you can write in it.

Activity 23: What's wrong?

Teaching notes for Level 1

Here are the important editing points in this passage, followed by a sample rewrite.

The accident

the[1] boy brok[2] his leg and he brok[3] his leg[4] in the park. and[5] then he went[6] hostipal[7] with his bad leg in the ambulance.[8] The doctor took a picture[9] of his leg and said it[10,11] is brokn[12] in pieces I will have to mend it right away it is an emergency we must do it quickly.[13,14] And[15] they did.[16] Now it is OK.[17]

Sample rewrite

The little boy was playing in the park when he broke his leg. He went in the ambulance to hospital. The doctor took an X-ray of his leg. 'Oh dear!' said the doctor. 'Your leg is very badly broken. This is an emergency and we must mend it very quickly.' So the doctor mended the boy's leg as soon as he could and now it is healed.

1 Capital letter needed.

2 Spelling.

3 Spelling.

4 Poor sentence structure: **the boy broke his leg and he broke his leg** is repetitive.

5 Sentence should not start with **and**, and capital letter needed.

6 Should be **went to hospital**.

7 Spelling.

8 Poor expression: **he went with his bad leg in the ambulance**.

9 Poor vocabulary: **X-ray** is better.

10 Speech marks and capital letter needed for doctor's statement.

11 Better to replace **it** with **your leg**.

12 Spelling.

13 Run-on sentence. See sample rewrite for an alternative.

14 Speech marks and full stop needed.

15 Sentence should not start with **and**.

16 **And they did** is not a sentence.

17 Colloquial **OK** should be avoided.

Activity 23

What's wrong?

LEVEL 1

Edit and rewrite this passage.

The accident

the boy brok his leg and he brok his leg in the park.

and then he went hostipal with his bad leg in the

ambulance. The doctor took a picture of his leg and

said it is brokn in pieces I will have to mend it right

away it is an emergency we must do it quickly. And

they did. Now it is OK.

Activity 23: What's wrong?

Teaching notes for Level 2

Here are the important editing points in this passage, followed by a sample rewrite.

Holiday horse riding

In the holdais[1] I went horsriding.[2] I brushed the horse. He was black.[3] I do not know his name.[4] I had a ride.[5] It was fun.[6] Katherine had a ride. It was fun. Ben had a ride. It was fun.[7] The horse was in the feld.[8] The horse galloped very fast like a racehorse.[9] After we went home.[10] We had a burger and fries on the way home.[11] I went to bed.[12]

Sample rewrite

In the holidays I went horse riding. I rode a beautiful black horse and I was allowed to brush him until his coat shone. I do not know his name, but maybe he was called something like 'Midnight' because he was so black. Katherine and Ben also had a ride. We all had a lot of fun because the horse galloped very fast, like a racehorse. On the way home from riding we had a burger and fries and then I went to bed and dreamt that I was riding Midnight at the Olympic Games.

---

1 Spelling.

2 Spelling.

3 Dull writing.

4 Dull writing.

5 Dull writing.

6 Dull writing.

7 Too much repetition of **had a ride. It was fun.**

8 Spelling.

9 Interesting writing: **galloped very fast like a racehorse**.

10 Flat, uninteresting and not connected to the title of **Holiday horse riding**.

11 Not connected to the title of **Holiday horse riding**.

12 Not connected to the title of **Holiday horse riding**.

Activity 23

What's wrong?

LEVEL 2

Edit and rewrite this passage.

Holiday horse riding

In the holdais I went horsriding. I brushed the

horse. He was black. I do not know his name. I had

a ride. It was fun. Katherine had a ride. It was fun.

Ben had a ride. It was fun. The horse was in the

feld. The horse galloped very fast like a racehorse.

After we went home. We had a burger and fries on

the way home. I went to bed.

Activity 23: What's wrong?

Teaching notes for Level 3

Here are the important editing points in this passage, followed by a sample rewrite.

Our mini Olympics

At school this week we had a mini Olympics. I walk[1] to the dais and stood on it to get my medal.[2] The principle[3] opened the Olympics and we all sang a song. Then we danced with ribbins.[4] Then we had a running race. Next I won a medal because I won the running race.[5] I felt very proud. We played with tennis racquets.[6] We did[7] basketball. Last[8] we did archery. We shot baskets and I got one in.[9] The Olymoics[10] is what they did in Greece.[11] But now we have them all the time[12] and in diffirint[13] countries like China and that.[14] And[15] we have sports like ice hockey and everything[16] in the Olympics. And they are on TV all the time.[17] And sailing.[18]

Sample rewrite

The Olympic Games were first held in Ancient Greece. Now we have the modern Olympic Games, which are held in different countries such as China, Australia or the USA, once every four years. When the Olympics are on there is usually total television coverage. Sailing, ice hockey and many other sports are part of the Olympics. At school this week we had a mini Olympics. The principal opened the Olympics and we all sang a song and danced with ribbons. Then we had a running race. I was very excited. I ran as fast as I could and won a medal for coming first. I stood on the dais to receive my medal and felt very proud. We played tennis and we played basketball. We shot balls and I got one in. Finally we did archery. We all enjoyed the mini Olympics.

1 Should be **walked** not **walk**.

2 Out of order in the story: the medal was awarded after the running race.

3 Spelling.

4 Spelling.

5 Poor structure: **then we had a running race. Next I won a medal because I won the running race**.

6 Better to say **played tennis** than **played with tennis racquets**.

7 Better to say **played basketball** than **did basketball**.

8 If archery was last it should be last in the account of the day.

9 The sentence about shooting baskets should follow the sentence about basketball.

10 Spelling.

11 This information might be better at the start of the passage.

12 Inaccurate statement: **regularly, every four years** or **frequently** would be more accurate.

13 Spelling.

14 Poor expression: **and that** could be replaced with the names of other Olympic host countries.

15 Not good to start a sentence with **And**.

16 Poor expression: **and everything** could be replaced with examples of other Olympic events.

17 Poor expression: see sample rewrite for a better version of this sentence.

18 **And sailing** is not a sentence. The information should be placed with the other examples of Olympic events.

Activity 23

What's wrong?

LEVEL 3

Edit and rewrite this passage.

Our mini Olympics

At school this week we had a mini Olympics. I walk to the dais and stood on it to get my medal. The principle opened the Olympics and we all sang a song. Then we danced with ribbins. Then we had a running race. Next I won a medal because I won the running race. I felt very proud. We played with tennis racquets. We did basketball. Lastly we did archery. We shot baskets and I got one in. The Olymoics is what they did in Greece. But now we have them all the time and in diffirint countries like China and that. And we have sports like ice hockey and everything in the Olympics. And they are on TV all the time. And sailing.